Beyond Beer Goggles: Interactive Teaching Methods for Alcohol, Other Drugs and AIDS Prevention

Fourth Edition

MARK J. MINELLI, Ph.D.
CENTRAL MICHIGAN UNIVERSITY

ISBN 978-1-58874-938-3

Published by
STIPES PUBLISHING L.L.C.
204 W. University Ave.
Champaign, Illinois 61820

DEDICATION

To my loving wife Debra who supports me in all my creative endeavors.

FORWARD

AIDS is nothing to worry about. Only THOSE people get it. I have heard this, and similar statements, since we first recognized that the syndrome had hit this country. This, in spite of the fact that in most of the world the vast majority of HIV/AIDS patients are heterosexuals. Indeed, the CDC says that AIDS is the number one cause of death in men ages 25 to 44 and the number four cause of death in women of the same age group. This is regardless of whether they are homosexual or heterosexual. In this country, the fastest growing HIV positive segments of the population are: Women, their babies, and teenagers.

There seems to be something in the human condition that wants us to deny that anything can happen to us. One way that we reinforce that is to segregate the population into groups and that way we can always say that it is the other group that is at risk. The history of AIDS is a good example of this behavior.

In the early days of this epidemic, it was called GRID (Gay Related Immune Deficiency). And, as long as it was THOSE people (i.e., Gays) that got GRID, the Reagan administration was able to ignore the problem. When IV drug users and certain immigrant groups were identified as having a high risk of contracting HIV, the same logic applied. The administration was able to ignore AIDS until it became obvious that large numbers of native born, white, heterosexual people were being diagnosed as HIV positive.

When this natural human tendency is reinforced by people in authority, and combined with the natural feelings of immortality so common in the young, the risk becomes unacceptably high for that age group.

We see the same sort of logic applied to regionalism as well. I have spent my entire professional life as a health care provider (the first 11 years in San Francisco). Upon moving to rural Michigan in 1989, it was like starting all over again. In spite of the fact that the CDC has estimated that by the year 2000, 80 percent of all new HIV infections in this country will come from rural areas, 80 to 90 percent of all the people I lecture to still seem to think of it as a big city problem that can't happen here.

Even though the problem of AIDS may be the single most important health care question to face America and its young people today, it is by no means the only one with life-altering consequences. Promiscuous sex, with all of the possibilities of contracting other sexually transmitted diseases, unwanted pregnancies, and the consequences to self-esteem, are certainly among them.

Alcohol, the most abused drug of our day, certainly factors into this equation. The lowering of inhibitions that usually accompanies alcohol use may increase the chances of having unprotected sex, or the sharing of contaminated needles. It also lowers the CD_4 cell count and provides a greater chance of contracting opportunistic diseases of all types.

Much has been written about how our popular culture glorifies alcohol abuse and promiscuous sex. It doesn't take the average observer long to see that myths abound in these areas. What isn't so apparent to the casual observer is that we do the same thing with other forms of drug abuse. And here too, it happens to other groups.

Cocaine use, although shown on documentaries to cut across all segments of society, and condemned because it is known to: Stimulate the brain to near seizure, cause extreme mood swings, raise blood pressure to dangerous levels, greatly increase heart rate, and/or induce irregular heart beat or heart stoppage, is often shown in popular fiction as the drug of choice among the rich and famous. At the same time and at the opposite end of the spectrum, children in the poorest neighborhoods see cocaine glamorized as a way to make fast money and get out of the ghetto. But somehow, it just isn't a white, middle class problem.

One theme runs through all of this. That is: The risks in all of these areas may be greatly reduced or eliminated altogether, based upon an individual's behavior. We know it can happen to someone else. What we now need is a way to show our young people that it CAN happen to them. This is why I was glad to see this book developed in this particular form.

Research has shown that interactive methods are among the best ways to impart information and develop wise decision-making skills. It does the former by making learning more fun than traditional lecture methods, and easier by involving more senses than lecture alone. It does the latter by forcing the student to think their way through problems and defend their conclusions, when necessary to their peers. Additionally, peer group feedback reinforces the values and ideas worked out through interaction. And, after all, it is our beliefs, values, and attitudes that determine our behavior.

By now it should be obvious to most observant adults that new and bolder steps need to be taken in our fight to educate young people to the dangers of contracting sexually transmitted diseases and substance abuse. The statistics show that we are losing this battle. I believe this book to be one small step towards winning the war.

-M. H. "Mark" Jones, M.A. (P.W.A.)
Deceased–October, 1995

Introduction

Research appears to indicate that optimal learning methods should incorporate all of the five senses (touch, taste, site, sound and smell). We also have discovered that people retain information most efficiently through a variety of learning techniques. Assessment tools have been designed to divulge if individuals can recall data best through reading, lectures, video, etc.

A review of the literature suggests that educational approaches to prevent alcohol and other drug (AOD) problems and Human Immunodeficiency Virus (HIV)/Acquired Immunodeficiency Syndrome (AIDS) infection should utilize peer resistant skills, decision making, peer educators, alternative activities, be culturally sensitive and specific and use HIV positive individuals to share their hopes, desires, and stories. A multi-dimensional approach to prevention is indicating the highest level of success in effectively dealing with these problems of immense magnitude.

This manual is an attempt to blend a variety of the aforementioned educational methods and techniques to better serve students in their learning process and to provide teachers with additional approaches to instruction. As opposed to providing factual or statistical information alone, a more interactive philosophical approach has been utilized in the development of this manual. It should also be noted that these activities should be approved by your administration, school board, or curriculum committees as health and human sexuality are very sensitive issues.

The majority of these learning activities have been used at the collegiate level with the students both enjoying and being more involved with the educational process. A special thank you is given to the many students at Central Michigan University that have provided ideas, concepts and activities incorporated within this document. They are too numerous to name individually, but the reader should be cognizant that peer empowerment has helped to shape this manual. We need to continue to be bold, provocative, and creative in dealing with AOD and HIV/AIDS prevention issues. Users of this manual are encouraged to design additional interactive activities to take learning to its most useful level.

How To Use This Book

This manual has been designed as a supplemental educational tool and it is to be used in conjunction with other reference materials. Statistics and the presentation of current scientific information have generally been avoided to require students to explore their thoughts, feelings, and beliefs. Most of the activities have been designed using a consistent format of objectives, materials needed, activity, educational theme, and references/further readings. Although some discussion questions have been provided, a more open ended approach has been incorporated to challenge students to go beyond facts and reach towards behavioral change and to seek their own solution to problems. Blending these interactive learning methods with lectures, videos, slides and other educational methods can provide students with an optimal environment to learn and to utilize information concerning AOD and HIV/AIDS.

As mentioned before, these activities should be approved by your administration, school board, or curriculum committee because of the sensitive nature of the content areas involved. These activities can be both enjoyable and intellectually stimulating. Teachers should strive to develop their own interactive methods based on the culture and environment in which they work.

TABLE OF CONTENTS

PART I

ALCOHOL AND OTHER DRUGS

Title of Activity **Page**

Brain Sponge Demonstration 1
Bulletin Boards 3
Cultural Perceptions Of Alcohol Use And Abuse 5
Cultural Perceptions Of Alcohol Use And Abuse Worksheet 7
Drunk Driving Tickets 9
You Have The Power To Stop Drunk Driving 11
Design A Law 13
Framing A Positive Picture 15
Grim Reaper 17
Jelly Bean Role Play 19
Mocktails 21
Name That Rock Star 23
Drug Testing And Your Business 25
How and Where Do You Store Your Medications 27
Home Safety Medication Storage Checklist 29
Invent A Drug To Help Mankind 31
Say Rap To Drugs 33
Side Effects Of Prescription Drugs 35
The Most Common Drugs 37
What Is The Most Dangerous Drug? 39
What I get From Smoking or Chewing Tobacco 41
Tobacco Fact Sheet 43
The Smoking Machine 45
Smokeless Tobacco And The Dentist 47
How Much Does It Cost To Smoke? 49
Alternatives to Anabolic-Androgenic Steroids 51
Gain or Lose The Competitive Edge 53
Rohypnol 55
Advertising 57
Becoming Energized For Good Health 59
Create Your Own Learning Strategy 61
Don't Embarrass Your Family 63
Empower Your Community 65
Look What We Put In Our Bodies 67
Nameplates 69

TABLE OF CONTENTS

PART I

ALCOHOL AND OTHER DRUGS

PAGE 2

Title of Activity **Page**

Personal Traits That Impress Me 71
Qualities Of Your Hero 73
Qualities Of Your Hero Worksheet 75
Risky Business 77
Risky Business Worksheet 79
What Can You Do To Prevent Drug Abuse? 81
What Would Happen If You Failed A Drug Test? 83
Rate Your Protective And Risk Factors 85
Rate Your Protective And Risk Factors Worksheet 87
If I Were Arrested 89
If I Were Arrested Worksheet 91
Ten Things You Like To Do 93
The Future 95
The Perfect Town/City 97
The Top Ten Songs 99
Wellness Punch Game 101
Advice Column for Substance Abuse Prevention 103
Computer Assisted Learning 105
Information Brochure 107
Marinol (Dronabinol) as Medicine 109
Drugs Used in Modern Medicine Worksheet 111
Invent a Label 113
Reaching Your Goals 115
Reaching Your Goals Worksheet 117
Peer Pressure 119
Drug Abuse in Sports 121
Baseball 123
Just Say Yes Too? 125
Body, Mind, and Spirit 127
Positive Ways to Handle Stress 129
Positive Ways to Handle Stress Worksheet 131
Internet Research 133
Internet Research Worksheet 135
Does Your Perception Become Your Reality? 137

TABLE OF CONTENTS

PART II

HUMAN IMMUNODEFICIENCY VIRUS (HIV)
ACQUIRED IMMUNODEFICIENCY SYNDROME (AIDS)
SEXUALLY TRANSMITTED DISEASE (STD)

Title of Activity	Page
Cultural/Age Group Specific HIV/AIDS Education	139
Facts In Motion	141
HIV Positive Guest Speaker	143
HIV/AIDS And Physics	145
HIV/AIDS High Risk Groups	147
How To Avoid HIV Risk Situations	149
Is This Safe?	151
Match The Answer	153
Predict The Future of HIV/AIDS	155
Crystal Ball Worksheet	157
Researching HIV/AIDS	159
Researching HIV/AIDS Worksheet	161
Taking Action To Prevent HIV/AIDS	163
Taking Action To Prevent HIV/AIDS Worksheet	165
The Body Bag	167
Too Hot To Handle	169
What's New On Film?	171
Critters That Grow On You	173
One In Five	175
Pick A Balloon	177
STD Mobile	179
Uglify An STD	181
Condom Size	183
Don't Use An Oil-Based Lubricant	185
Nine Steps To Condom Use	187
The Condom Relay Race	189
Time That Condom	191
Create Your Own Learning Strategy	193
Guess The Term	195
I Failed To Mention	197
Just Say No To Sex	199
Safer Sex While Intoxicated?	201

TABLE OF CONTENTS

PART II

HUMAN IMMUNODEFICIENCY VIRUS (HIV)
ACQUIRED IMMUNODEFICIENCY SYNDROME (AIDS)
SEXUALLY TRANSMITTED DISEASE (STD)

PAGE 2

Title of Activity **Page**

Sex Posters 203
Sexopoly 205
Sexual Relations Can Have Many Consequences 207
Too Much Sex On TV 209
Universal Precautions Equipment 211
Why Abstinence Is Cool 213
Write Your Own Public Service Announcements 215
Letter To The Editor 217
Excuses, Excuses 219
A – Z about HIV/AIDS 221
Thumbs Up/Down about AIDS 223
Cartoons Can Teach 225
Persuasive Commercial 227
AIDS Mapping 229
The Origin Of HIV/AIDS 231
HIV/AIDS Acronyms 233
Inhibit the Replication of HIV 235
Anonymous 237
Select A Country 239
Fighting Prejudice And Stigmas 241

About the Author 243
Beyond Beer Goggles Suggested Internet Resource Sites 245
References 249

PART I

ALCOHOL AND OTHER DRUGS

"BRAIN SPONGE DEMONSTRATION"

Objective(s)

1. Students will view how poor decisions can be made while using alcohol or other drugs.
2. Students will see a demonstration of the human brain storing information.

Materials

- Large sponge
- Pan of water

Activity

1. Ask for a student volunteer from the class. Have the student hold the sponge up (so the class can see) and say that the sponge is like the human brain at birth—void of a lot of information about life.
2. Have the student place the sponge in the pan of water and explain that as we grow, our brain takes in and learns a variety of new information.
3. Have the student take the sponge out of the water and drain the water out. Just as the sponge loses water, the brain often disregards important information that can place you in risky situations when using alcohol or other drugs.
4. Have students provide examples of this disregard of important information.

Educational Theme

- People often disregard important information and place themselves in risky situations when using alcohol and other drugs.

Resources

1. Koob, G. and Moal, M., *Neurobiology of Addiction*. London: Academic Press, 2005.

"BULLETIN BOARDS"

Objective(s)

1. Students will design bulletin boards with messages on alcohol or other drug abuse.

Materials Needed

- Bulletin board
- Variety of materials

Activity

1. Have students take turns, in pairs, to design bulletin boards relating to alcohol or other drug abuse. (This could be used as extra credit or part of a class requirement.)

Educational Theme

- A variety of health topics can be presented in a visual learning format.

"CULTURAL PERCEPTIONS OF ALCOHOL USE AND ABUSE"

Objective(s)

1. Students will investigate and report on various cultures and their use or non-use of alcoholic beverages.

Materials Needed

- Paper and pencil
- "Cultural Perceptions of Alcohol Use and Abuse" Worksheet (see following page)

Activity

1. Explain to the students that various cultures have different perspectives on their use or non-use of alcoholic beverages. These differences involving alcohol include ceremonies, customs, socialization patterns, etc.

2. Have the students talk with their relatives, friends or others they know concerning these issues using the worksheet "Cultural Perspectives On Alcohol Use." After the students have completed their interviews, they can report back to the class and have a chance to hear about other families and cultures.

3. Provide an overview of the various differences and similarities involving alcohol use and non-use in relationship to family and cultural norms. Other research can be presented to enrich what the students have discovered in their interviews.

Educational Theme

- Various cultures have different perspectives on their use or non-use of alcoholic beverages.

Resources

1. Ray, O. and Ksir, C. *Drugs, Society and Human Behavior*, (12th Ed.), Boston: McGraw-Hill, 2003.

2. McKim, W. *Drugs and Behavior*, (6th Ed.), Upper Saddle River, N.J.: Prentice Hall, 2006.

"CULTURAL PERCEPTIONS OF ALCOHOL USE AND ABUSE WORKSHEET"

Person Interviewed: ______________________________

Relationship to Interviewee: ______________________________

1. How is alcohol use or non-use viewed in your family or cultural ethnic background?

2. What types of ceremonies, customs, etc., involve alcohol? How or why is alcohol used for these events?

3. How is drunkenness viewed by your family or cultural ethnic background?

"DRUNK DRIVING TICKETS"

Objective(s)

1. Students will review the local laws for drunk driving by reading current court cases and press releases.

Materials Needed

- Local newspapers
- Copy of your State or local laws involving drunk driving

Activity

1. Have the students bring in local newspaper clippings from the district or circuit court sections to review typical sentences involving drunk driving. They may also include other articles relating to traffic fatalities or injuries involving alcohol.

2. Ask the students the following questions: What are the typical fines, jail time, etc., associated with a drunk driving ticket? Are there hidden costs like insurance increases, reinstatement of your license, drunk driving school classes, etc., that may not appear in the newspaper? Would it be embarrassing to have your name appear in the local paper? How would it feel . . . ?

Educational Theme

- As drunk driving is a major killer for young people, the price you could pay for breaking the law may be costly.

Resources

1. A local police officer familiar with current state and local laws involving drunk driving.

"YOU HAVE THE POWER TO STOP DRUNK DRIVING"

Objective(s)

1. Students will share ideas on how to intervene with a friend that has overindulged with alcohol and plans to drive.

Materials

- Chalkboard or whiteboard, eraser, and chalk or markers

Activity

1. Tell the students that they are at a party in which one of their friends has drank too much and plans to drive home. Brainstorm out loud, by using a chalkboard, and create a listing of ideas they have that would keep their intoxicated friend from driving.

Educational Theme

- You have the power to intervene and keep someone from driving drunk.

Resources

1. VanTuyl, C. *Drunk Driving: Issues That Concern You*, Farmington Hills, MI: Greenhaven Press, 2006.

2. Thompson, T. *Drunk Driving*, Farmington Hills, MI: Greenhaven Press, 2007.

"DESIGN A LAW"

Objective(s)

1. Students will design a law that will help reduce drinking and driving.

Materials Needed

- ➢ Paper and pencil
- ➢ Copy of current state drunk driving laws

Activity

1. Have each student write and design a law that they feel would help reduce drinking and driving injuries and fatalities. Describe the penalties and fines involved including:

Percent of Alcohol Level in Bloodstream		________
Penalties:	Jail Time	________
	Fines	________
	Community Services Hours	________
	Substance Abuse Screening	________
	Other Fines or Penalties (Example: colored drunk driver license plate)	________

2. Students can share their laws with fellow classmates and compare with current state laws.

Educational Theme

- ➢ Changes in public laws, policies and practices can help create environments that decrease the probability of drunk driving.

Resources

1. Center for Substance Abuse Prevention, http://prevention.samhsa.gov/.
2. Copies of current state drinking and driving laws.

"FRAMING A POSITIVE PICTURE"

Objective(s)

1. Students will see that their fellow classmates do not binge drink or drink on a daily basis.

Materials Needed

- Poster Board
- Magic Markers
- Current local or national alcohol use survey data

Activity

1. Review current alcohol use data from surveys appropriate to your students age group. (If you find that 4 percent of college students drink on a daily basis, reverse this to show that 96 percent do not drink on a daily basis.)

2. Ask, from the review of surveys, how many students drink on a daily basis. Findings can be placed on the front of the poster board with answers on the reverse side. Interesting statistics can be shown that the majority of students do not abuse alcohol or other drugs.

Educational Theme

- People's perceptions often become their reality even if they are not based on factual information.

Resources

1. Current local, state, or national alcohol use surveys.

"GRIM REAPER"

Objectives

1. Students will understand the consequences of alcohol abuse.

2. Students will observe potential results of drunk driving, alcohol over-dose, etc.

Materials Needed:

*Costume: Gown (black)
Hood (black)
Gloves (white)
Mask
Sickle (optional)

*Distribution Materials: Alcohol Awareness Pamphlets and Bookmarks

Activity

1. Recruit a person to dress in a grim reaper costume, the individual walks around campus or in a high pedestrian traffic area and distributes alcohol awareness materials. No verbal communication is necessary to represent the extreme consequences that may result from alcohol abuse. Contact with the mass media may be beneficial to create prior awareness of activity. The grim reaper can be used for: Conferences, mock wake, mock cemetery, radio talk show co-host, etc.

Educational Theme

➢ Alcohol abuse can have many serious consequences.

Designed by: David J. Urlaub

"JELLY BEAN ROLE PLAY"

Objective(s)

1. Students will practice saying no to alcohol and drugs.

2. Students will see how peer pressure can make it difficult to resist using alcohol and drugs.

Materials Needed

- Assorted jelly beans or candies

Activity

1. Ask for a student volunteer from the group and tell this person to resist whatever the group tells them to do.

2. Have some students sit in a circle with your volunteer. Tell the group to pretend the jelly beans represent alcohol or drugs and try to encourage the volunteer to take some. No touching or forcing the volunteer is allowed.

3. Discuss the activity after the roll play situation is completed or goes on for a few minutes. Was the pressure to use intense? What avenues or techniques were used by the groups to try and make the volunteer eat the jelly beans?

Educational Theme

- Peer pressure can be very intense at times, but can be overcome with a personal plan or a positive, determined attitude.

Resources

1. Minelli, M. and Breckon, D. *Community Health Education: Settings, Roles and Skills,* (5th Ed.) Sudbury, MA: Jones and Bartlett, 2009.

2. Pirsig, R. M. *LILA: A Inquiry Into Morals*, New York, Bantam Books, 1991.

"MOCKTAILS"

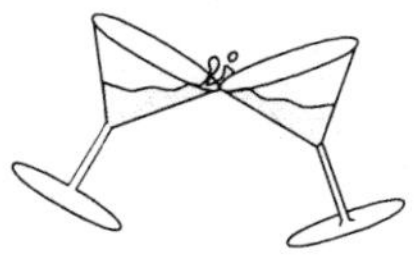

Objective(s)

1. Students will create a non-alcoholic drink to share with classmates.

Materials Needed

➢ Recipes of Mocktails

Activity

1. Have students make up mocktail or non-alcoholic drinks they can share with classmates. Recipes should be written down so the facilitator can create a master list of these beverages.

2. Develop a list of commercial non-alcoholic beers and wines.

Educational Theme

➢ Mocktails can serve as an alternative to alcoholic beverages.

Resources

1. Tyler Herbst, S. *The Ultimate Liquor-Free Drink Guide*, New York: Broadway, 2002.

"NAME THAT ROCK STAR"

Objective(s)

1. Students will name rock stars that have overdosed and died from alcohol and drug abuse.

Materials Needed

➢ Chalkboard or whiteboard, chalk or markers, eraser

Activity

1. Ask the students to name rock stars that have overdosed or died of alcohol or other drug abuse (i.e., Jimi Hendrix, Elvis Presley, Janis Joplin, John Bonham, Jim Morrison, etc.). Place names on the chalkboard, explain that even though these people reached stardom, alcohol and drugs can be bigger than they were.

Educational Theme

➢ Alcohol and other drug abuse can ruin lives regardless of a person's fame and fortune.

"DRUG TESTING AND YOUR BUSINESS"

Objective(s)

1. Students will observe the decision making process and pros and cons in regards to drug testing.

Materials Needed

- None

Activity

1. Have five or six students volunteer for a role play. Tell them they have just begun a new business and they are the board of directors.

2. Tell the volunteers they will need to decide if they are going to drug test all employees, only new employees after they are hired, only after an accident, or not to use drug testing.

3. Have a class discussion on what they observed during this process; did the group reach consensus? Would there be potential legal problems with their decision? Was it difficult to come to consensus?

Educational Theme

- Many companies are drug testing employees and people should be aware that they may be drug tested sometime during their career.

Resources

1. Maisto, S., Galizio, M. and Connors, G. *Drug Use and Abuse*, (5th Ed.), Florence, KY: Wadsworth Publishing, 2007.

2. Goldberg, R. *Drugs Across the Spectrum*, (5th Ed.), Belmont, CA: Thomson Wadsworth, 2006.

"HOW AND WHERE DO YOU STORE YOUR MEDICATIONS"

Objective(s)

1. Students will investigate how and where they store their medications at home.

2. Students will learn safe methods of storing medications.

Materials Needed

- Paper and pencils

- Home Safety Medication Storage Checklist (see following page)

Activity

1. Send the Safety Checklist home with the students to help assess how and where they store their household medications.

2. Ask, upon completion of their investigation and the students have turned in the checklist:

   a. What did you learn through this home study?

   b. Did you make any changes on where these items are stored?

Educational Theme

- Prescription and nonprescription medications must be properly stored in the home to insure user safety.

Resources

1. Adapted from: Mid-State Substance Abuse Commission, Duncan Series, 1993. Used with permission.

HOME SAFETY MEDICATION STORAGE CHECKLIST

(Circle Your Answers)

1.	Are all medications locked or secured?	Yes	No
2.	Are medications out of the reach of small children?	Yes	No
3.	Are any medications left out on tables, shelves, or nightstands?	Yes	No
4.	Are outdated medications discarded?	Yes	No
5.	Are all medication bottles labeled?	Yes	No
6.	Are all medications out of direct sunlight?	Yes	No

"INVENT A DRUG TO HELP HUMANKIND"

Objective(s)

1. Students will pretend to invent a new drug that cures a known medical condition or disease.

2. Students will review that many prescription and non-prescription drugs are used to treat disease and illness.

Materials Needed

- Paper and pencil

Activity

1. Explain to the students and give examples that many drugs are used to treat disease and illness. Example: Aspirin (treats headaches and mild pain); penicillin (treats specific infections).

2. Tell the students they can invent any drug they wish and explain what it is used for. Please have them use the following outline:

   Name of the drug
   What this drug is used for
   How is the drug taken (pill, liquid, etc.)
   How long is the drug to be taken
   Potential side effects
   Cost per prescription

3. Have students explain their drug creations and uses with their classmates.

Educational Theme

- Drugs are used and are currently being developed to treat disease and illness.

Resources

1. *Physicians Desk Reference*, Montvale, NJ: Thompson PDR, 2007.

"SAY RAP TO DRUGS"

Objective(s)

1. Students will create and perform a rap song with an anti-drug theme.

Materials Needed

- Tape or CD player
- Rap tape without words

Activity

1. Have students, singly or in pairs, write and perform an anti-drug rap song. Give students the options to sing "rock & roll" or other styles of music. If the students have a difficult time creating an original song, they could select a pre-recorded tune.

Educational Theme

- Songs can celebrate staying alcohol and other drug-free.

Resources

1. Copies of *Billboard Magazine*.

"SIDE EFFECTS OF PRESCRIPTION DRUGS"

Objective(s)

1. Students will state the uses and abuses of prescription drugs.

Materials Needed

- Various text books on prescription drugs.

Activity

1. Ask students to pick a prescription drug they have taken before, or are interested in, to learn more about.

2. Instruct students, as they do their research, to use the following outline:

   Name of the Drug:
   Medical Uses:
   Potential Side Effects:
   Not To Be Used In Combination With:
   Price:

3. Ask students, after they have collected their information, to share the reports with their classmates.

4. Point out that prescription drugs can have a variety of uses but can also be abused or have unwanted side effects.

Educational Theme

- Prescription drugs have been developed to cure diseases, reduce suffering and improve the quality of life. As they often have side effects, they need to be monitored closely and taken only as prescribed.

Resources

1. *Drug Facts and Comparisons*, 2009, St. Louis, MO: Lippincott Raven, 2008.

"THE MOST COMMON DRUGS"

Objective(s)

1. Students will develop a listing of what the most common drugs of use and abuse are.

2. Students will discuss and analyze the final drug listing.

Materials Needed

- Chalkboard or whiteboard, chalk or markers, and eraser

- Drug use listing from the National Institute on Drug Abuse or University of Michigan Social Research Institute

Activity

1. List on the chalkboard many of the commonly used and abused drugs in America (i.e., alcohol, heroin, caffeine, tobacco, cocaine, anabolic steroids, hallucinogens, marijuana, etc.).

2. Ask, for among the top three or four listed, what are the similarities? Differences? Costs? Etc. What are some conclusions you can make as a group? How does your list compare to the national drug ranking lists?

3. Pose to students: If you were to ask ten people in the hall and they were totally honest, in the last month how often have they used alcohol? Have the students just say out loud seven out of ten or three out of ten, etc.

Educational Theme

- The most commonly abused drugs in America are the legal substances.

Resources

1. Current drug use listing from the National Institute on Drug Abuse or University of Michigan Social Research Institute.

"WHAT IS THE MOST DANGEROUS DRUG?"

Objective(s)

1. Students will explore with others what they believe to be the most dangerous drug.

2. Students will acquire knowledge about various drugs.

Materials Needed

- Paper and pencils

Activity

1. Have students ask others (friend, parents, etc.), as a homework assignment, what they consider the most dangerous drug, and what they base this belief on. Write this information down to bring back to class.

2. From the information collected, create a list of the drugs and numbers of times they are mentioned. When the list is complete, see which drug was mentioned the most times. Ask, "Is this drug an illegal or legal drug?", "What are the comments made about this drug?", "Are there any useful purposes for this drug?"

Educational Theme

- Drugs have many effects on the human body. Some drugs can be both life saving or threatening, depending on use and dosage.

Resources

1. Fields, R. *Drugs and Alcohol in Perspective*, (7th Ed.), Boston: McGraw-Hill, 2010.

2. Website <http://ncadi.samhsa.gov/> Prevention Online: Substance Abuse and Mental Health Service Administration's National Clearinghouse for Alcohol and Drug Information.

"WHAT I GET FROM SMOKING OR CHEWING TOBACCO"

Objective(s)

1. Students will recite a variety of effects from cigarette smoking or chewing tobacco.

Materials Needed

- " Tobacco Fact Sheet" (see following page)

Activity

1. Cut the fact sheet into 14 individual facts and have the students select (from a hat, box, etc.) one. Ask students to read their selection out loud. Discussions about the "fact sheet" can follow the exercise.

Educational Theme

- Both cigarette smoking and chewing tobacco can create unhealthy living conditions and impair optimal personal health.

Resources

1. See previous resources cited in activities on cigarette and chewing tobacco use.

2. Website <www.cdc.gov/tobacco/index.htm> Center for Disease Control and Prevention – Smoking and Tobacco Use.

3. Website <www.lungusa.org/site/c.dvLUK9Ooe/b.22542/k.CA6A.Home.htm> American Lung Association.

"TOBACCO FACT SHEET"

1. I smoke and I have brown stained teeth.
2. I smoke and I have yellow stained fingers where I hold my cigarette.
3. I inhale cigarettes and I cough a lot, and have a hard time breathing.
4. Nicotine kills over 400,000 Americans a year; I hope I'm not one of them.
5. You know they've used nicotine before in insecticides, I wonder how I can get more bugs to smoke?
6. You know what they say, another nail in the coffin.
7. I'm chewing right now, how about a great big kiss!
8. Look, my gums are receding.
9. What's this white patch in my mouth?
10. If chewing tobacco tasted so good, don't you think they'd make tobacco flavored gum?
11. Where do I spit this stuff?
12. Nicotine is one of the most addictive drugs.
13. If I smoke when I'm pregnant, will it hurt my baby?
14. Give me another cancer stick.

"THE SMOKING MACHINE"

Objective(s)

1. Students will demonstrate how tobacco smoke fills the lungs.

Materials Needed

- Any smoking demonstration model available through a variety of health supply catalogs.
- Cigarette

Activity

1. Follow the instructions on the smoking demonstration model and ask a student volunteer to assist. As the model smokes the cigarette, the clear container will fill with smoke like our lungs do.
2. Blow cigarette smoke through a tissue paper; observe what is left on the paper.

Educational Theme

- It is often difficult to observe what happens to our bodies when using AOD.

Resources

1. Website <www.quitnet.org> Quit Net.
2. Website <www.tobaccofree.org> The Foundation for a Smokefree America.

"SMOKELESS TOBACCO AND THE DENTIST"

Objective(s)

1. Students will learn the negative effects of smokeless tobacco products in relation to the mouth.

Materials Needed

- "Mr. Gross Mouth" model (can be purchased from: Health Edco, PO Box 21207, Waco, TX 76702-1207. Phone: (1-800-299-3366.)

Activity

1. Discuss some of the negative consequences of smokeless tobacco, then select a student volunteer to play the role of the dentist. (Use the model, "Mr. Gross Mouth," which lists the negative effects on it, this should be easy for the student to identify problems.)

2. Ask the student "Dr. Painless" to come and look at this person, "Mr. Gross Mouth" and ask the student questions, like, "What kinds of problems do you see?" "Will this cost a lot of money to repair" "Is there any hope?"

Educational Theme

- The use of smokeless tobacco products can be both costly to your health and pocketbook.

Resources

1. Minelli, M. *Drug Abuse in Sports: A Student Course Manual*, (7th Ed.), Champaign, IL: Stipes Publishing, 2008.

"HOW MUCH DOES IT COST TO SMOKE?"

Objective(s)

1. Students will estimate the cost of smoking cigarettes.

2. Students will develop a list of other things they could purchase with the estimated money saved if not smoking.

Materials Needed

- Calculator

- Paper and pencils

Activity

1. Give one of the students in the classroom a calculator.

2. Estimate the current price of a package of cigarettes in your area (i.e., $5.30 per pack.)

3. Give examples: If I smoked a pack of cigarettes a day, what would that cost me in a year? $1,934.50. What if I smoked two packs a day each year? $3,869.

4. Ask each student to use these figures and predict what other kinds of things they could purchase with this money (i.e., stereo systems, car payments, clothes, etc.). Have some students share their list with their fellow classmates.

Educational Theme

- Although the health risks associated with cigarette smoking are well documented, the actual cost of smoking is often not considered.

Resources

1. Goode, E. *Drugs in American Society*, (7th Ed.), Boston: McGraw Hill, 2007.

"ALTERNATIVES TO ANABOLIC-ANDROGENIC STEROIDS"

Objective(s)

1. Students will brainstorm various alternatives to the use of anabolic-androgenic steroids.

Materials Needed

- Chalkboard or whiteboard, chalk or markers, and eraser

Activity

1. Explain to the students that sometimes athletes use anabolic-androgenic steroids in hopes of gaining a competitive edge on their competition. Not only are there serious risks to human health with abuse of these substances (such as cardiovascular system impairment, etc.), but their use is considered cheating by all major athletic associations, leagues, etc.

2. Have the students collectively brainstorm and list legal ways athletes could enhance their performance level or skills. Write their ideas on the chalk board.

Educational Theme

- Abuse of anabolic-androgenic steroids is considered a serious risk to human health and is also viewed as cheating by all major athletic associations.

Resources

1. Antonio, J., and Stout, J. *Sports Supplements*, Philadelphia: Lippincott Williams & Wilkins, 2001.

"GAIN OR LOSE THE COMPETITIVE EDGE"

Objective(s)

1. Students will decide if they would risk their health to potentially enhance athletic performance.

Materials Needed

- Paper and pencils
- Chalkboard or whiteboard, chalk or markers, and eraser

Activity

1. Have the students take out a piece of paper and ask them, "If I could give you a drug that would enhance your performance, but may cause a variety of health problems, would you take it?" Just mark a yes or no on the paper and hand it to the teacher or student assistant.

2. Write total yes and no responses on the chalkboard. Were there any yes answers? Ask why might people risk their health to potentially gain a competitive edge in athletic competition?

Educational Theme

- Some people will use performance enhancing drugs even if it risks their health.

Resources

1. Gerdes, L. *Performance Enhancing Drugs*, Farmington Hills, MI: Greenhaven Press, 2007.

"ROHYPNOL"

Objective(s)

1. Students will be aware of how Rohypnol (flunitrazepam) is used in potential date rape situations.

2. Students will role play saying no to high risk situations.

Materials

- Paper and pencil

Activity

1. Tell the students that the drug, Rohypnol, a sedative drug ten times stronger than valium, has been used to lace alcoholic and non-alcoholic drinks to take advantage of disabled women. This drug is also called the "forget pill" and wipes the memory clean, making it difficult to press charges if it turns out to be a date rape situation.

2. Have the students individually write responses on how they would observe and take action if they were at a party and wanted to keep a close eye on their drink? What would they do if a friend appeared extremely intoxicated at a party?

3. After students have completed the writing assignments they could take turns giving suggestions on how they would handle these types of situations.

Educational Theme

- The drug, Rohypnol, can easily be placed in alcoholic and non-alcoholic drinks to take advantage of disabled women. Individuals need to be aware of this new drug and pay close attention in party situations.

"ADVERTISING"

Objective(s)

1. Students will identify what message an advertising firm is trying to communicate in the promotion of alcohol or tobacco products.

Materials Needed

➢ Clip out current alcohol or tobacco advertisements from a variety of popular magazines, with different target audiences.

Activity

1. Show or pass out the alcohol and tobacco advertisements to your classroom. Have them describe what points or themes the company is attempting to promote.

Educational Theme

➢ Advertisers often equate the use of alcoholic beverages with sexual attractiveness, power, and success while neglecting to identify the risks associated with the misuse of alcohol or other drugs.

Resources

1. Mid-State Substance Abuse Commission, "Putting the Pieces Together," 1991.

"BECOMING ENERGIZED FOR GOOD HEALTH"

Objective(s)

1. Students will state their plan to become energized to follow a good health habit.

2. Students will share a positive health habit with their classmates.

Materials Needed

➢ Chalkboard or whiteboard, chalk or markers, and eraser

Activity

1. Tell the students they will need to first think of and then share a way they plan (or activities they are currently involved with) to become energized for good health. Examples could include jogging, lifting weights, practicing relaxation, etc.

2. Ask the students to identify many of the benefits of good health.

3. Ask the students to share their positive health habits, write each one on the chalkboard. After all the students have discussed their ideas, the instructor can point out the wide variety of things you can do to create good health habits.

4. Type all ideas generated and give to students as a handout.

Educational Theme

➢ Good health habits are a choice and can be fun to incorporate in your lifestyle.

Resources

1. Website <www.ama-assn.org> American Medical Association (AMA).

"CREATE YOUR OWN LEARNING STRATEGY"

Objective(s)

1. Students will create their own active learning method (can be used for any health-related topic).

Materials Needed

- Will be presented or described by the student.

Activity

1. Provide the students with some examples of active learning techniques then challenge the students to design and present their own. This can become part of a report on a health topic and can be done in teams if students are too anxious or embarrassed to present on their own.

Educational Theme

- Peer education is an effective means in presenting information on health topics and issues.

Resources

1. Website <www.bacchusgamma.org> The Baccus and Gamma Peer Education Network.

2. Eta Sigma Gamma, *Project Direction*, Ball State University, 1991.

"DON'T EMBARRASS YOUR FAMILY"

Objective(s)

1. Students will state what kinds of social problems might embarrass their families or guardians.

Materials Needed

➢ Paper and pencils

Activity

1. Ask the students to write about what types of social problems they might encounter that could embarrass their family or guardians (i.e., drug bust, teen pregnancy, drunk driving charge).

2. Select some students to share their thoughts.

3. Ask the students the following questions:

   a. Are these problems avoidable?
   b. Do you know people these things have happened to?
   c. Can you take actions not to place yourself in trouble situations?

Educational Theme

➢ People should always consider how getting into trouble could embarrass their family, guardians, or friends.

"EMPOWER YOUR COMMUNITY"

Objective(s)

1. Students will explain what it would be like to empower their community in preventing AOD abuse.

Materials Needed

- Large writing pads
- Magic markers

Activity

1. Have students break into small discussion groups.
2. Ask them to develop lists of what they would do to empower their communities towards AOD prevention. Give the group 15 to 30 minutes each.
3. Have each small group present their lists back to the large group for comparisons and discussion.

Educational Theme

- Individuals have the power to shape the communities in which they live.

Resources

1. Edberg, M. "Essentials of Health Behavior: Social and Behavioral Theory" in *Public Health*, Sudbury, MA: Jones and Bartlett, 2007.

"LOOK WHAT WE PUT IN OUR BODIES"

Objective(s)

1. Students will view the difference between healthy and non-healthy choices that we can make.

Materials Needed

- Two large clear bowls
- A variety of legal substances the teacher provides (i.e., chewing tobacco, alcohol, OTC medicines, etc.)
- A variety of healthy, nutritional choices (i.e., fruits, vegetables, etc.)
- Large spoon

Activity

1. Place your two large clear bowls on a table in front of the class. Have the students take turns putting the healthy choices in a bowl and the non-healthy choices in another bowl.
2. Ask for a volunteer to come to the front of the classroom and stir the contents of each bowl. Follow this activity with a classroom discussion (i.e., what do you see? Is this what your stomach might look like after ingesting these items?).

Educational Theme

- We are what we eat. What would you rather have in your stomach?

Resources

1. Books on anatomy/physiology of the human body.

"NAMEPLATES"

Objective(s)

1. Students will give examples of their favorite hobbies and understand the relationship with AOD prevention activities.

Materials Needed

- Poster Board for nameplates
- Magic markers

Activity

1. Have all students, during the start of the first session, put their names and favorite hobbies (can use drawings) on their nameplates. After this, go around the room and have the students introduce themselves and tell about their hobbies.

2. Ask them, "What does this have to do with AOD prevention?" The answer is that alternatives or natural highs have been shown to be an effective means of AOD prevention.

Educational Theme

- Natural highs can be fun, entertaining, and an effective means of preventing AOD problems.

Resources

1. Website <www.jointogether.org> Join Together.

2. Website <www.casacolumbia.org) The National Center on Addiction and Substance Abuse at Columbia University.

"PERSONAL TRAITS THAT IMPRESS ME"

Objective(s)

1. Students will write a list of personal traits that impress them (i.e., honesty, intelligence, sense of humor).

Materials Needed

- Paper and pencils
- Chalkboard or whiteboard, chalk or markers, and eraser

Activity

1. Have each student develop a list of personal traits that impress them. After they have completed this listing, compile a rank order listing of the most common responses to share with the class. Most people are curious as to what impresses their friends, so this activity should have their attention. Remind the class that this is their rank ordering. Then ask if things like "Party Animal" or "Stoner" are on this list, or are they very popular as a personal trait?

Educational Theme

- Personal traits that impress the majority of people usually don't include things like "Party Animal," "stoner" or other terms that refer to abusers.

Resources

1. Hanson, G., and Venturelli, P. and Fleckenstein, A. *Drugs and Society*, (9th Ed.), Sudbury, MA: Jones, and Bartlett Publications, 2006.

"QUALITIES OF YOUR HERO"

Objective(s)

1. Students will list the qualities of one of their favorite heros.

Materials Needed

- Qualities of Your Hero Worksheet (see following page)
- Pencil

Activity

1. Have the students complete the "Qualities of Your Hero" worksheet.
2. Have students share their heros and qualities found within these individuals or do some self-reflection.
3. Ask questions such as:

    a. How many heros are sports personalities? Movie stars? Etc.
    b. Did AOD abuse play a role in their careers?
    c. What kinds of qualities did you mention?

Educational Theme

- Qualities of a hero usually do not include AOD abuse problems.

Materials Needed

QUALITIES OF YOUR HERO WORKSHEET

- Hero's Name ____

- What does (or did) this person do?

  ____

- List some personal qualities exhibited by your hero below.

  ____

  ____

  ____

  ____

  ____

  ____

  ____

  ____

"RISKY BUSINESS"

Objective(s)

1. Students will define what risky business means to them and what they can do to avoid high risk behaviors.

Materials Needed

- Pencils
- "Risky Business Worksheet" (see following page)

Activity

1. Have students complete the "Risky Business Worksheet." This worksheet will give students a chance to name high risk behaviors and explore alternatives.

2. Ask students to share their worksheets with classmates when completed. The instructor may want to examine which situations are most common and creative ways to cope with them.

Educational Theme

- Although there are many situations that may lead to a risky or health threatening situation, there are usually alternatives.

Resources

1. Website <www.nida.nih.gov> The National Institute on Drug Abuse.

2. Website <www.niaaa.nih.gov> The National Institute on Alcohol Abuse and Alcoholism.

"RISKY BUSINESS WORKSHEET"

List potential high risk behaviors that could affect your health.

List potential solutions to the high risk behaviors mentioned above.

"WHAT CAN YOU DO TO PREVENT DRUG ABUSE?"

Objective(s)

1. Students will plan and discuss action strategies they can incorporate into their lives to prevent drug abuse.

Materials

- Pencil and paper

Activity

1. Have the students break up into small discussion groups and make a list of ideas to prevent drug abuse. Choose a group recorder to share with the entire class the group's findings. Are there themes that have come up more than in one group? Make a master list to discuss with the class as a whole.

Educational Theme

- You have the power to shape your own life and prevent drug abuse.

"WHAT WOULD HAPPEN IF YOU FAILED A DRUG TEST?"

Objective(s)

1. Students will reflect and discuss what would happen to them if they failed a drug test.

Materials

- ➤ Paper and pencil

Activity

1. Tell the students that many companies and even some fast food restaurants are doing pre-employment drug testing, and sometimes testing on the job. Share with them that drugs stay in the human body (and can be detected) for different lengths of time.

2. Ask each student to write what they think would happen to them if they failed a drug test. Have students discuss their findings in class with other students.

Educational Theme

- ➤ There can be a personal price to pay if you are found to have drugs in your system after completing a drug screening test.

Resources

1. Website <www.dol.gov/index.htm> U.S. Department of Labor's Working Partners for an Alcohol and Drug Free Workplace.

"RATE YOUR PROTECTIVE AND RISK FACTORS"

Objective(s)

1. Students will rate their personal protective and risk factors for substance abuse.
2. Students will assess if they may need help due to the information they have discovered.

Materials

- Pencil
- "*Rate Your Protective and Risk Factors*" *Worksheet* (see following page)

Activity

1. As a homework assignment or in class, have each student complete the "*Rate Your Protective and Risk Factors*" *Worksheet*. If students find they have more risk than protective factors, they should think about seeking help.
2. To have the students be honest with themselves, they should not have to turn their worksheets in to the instructor.

Educational Theme

- Personal protective and risk factors can assist in determining your potential for substance abuse problems.

Resources

1. Website <www.drughelp.org> Phoenix House
2. Listing of local counseling agencies and self-help groups.

"RATE YOUR PROTECTIVE AND RISK FACTORS" WORKSHEET

Place a check mark next to any protective or risk factor you may have.

Protective Factors	Risk Factors
___ 1. I plan to continue my education.	___ 1. I do not do well in school or sometimes skip classes.
___ 2. I attend a school with clear rules and regulations.	___ 2. My school has a negative climate and I do not feel safe.
___ 3. I have a good sense of humor.	___ 3. I feel alone and alienated.
___ 4. I care about other people's feelings.	___ 4. I don't care what others think about me.
___ 5. I am involved in before or after-school activities.	___ 5. I do not get involved with before or after school activities.
___ 6. I have the ability to set goals and feel good about my future.	___ 6. I have few goals and do not feel good about my future.
___ 7. I can say no to people when I need to.	___ 7. I have a hard time saying no to my friends even if it may cause trouble.
___ 8. Most of my close friends do not drink or use tobacco products on a regular basis.	___ 8. Most of my friends drink and use tobacco products on a regular basis.
___ 9. My family has a moderate to upper income level.	___ 9. My family would be considered at a lower income level.
___ 10. I believe I could get a job if I tried.	___ 10. I believe I could not get a job if I tried.
___ 11. My parent(s) or guardian(s) keep a close eye on me.	___ 11. My parent(s) or guardian(s) do not keep a close eye on me.
___ 12. I belong to a church or religious affiliation.	___ 12. I do not belong to a church or religious affiliation.
___ 13. My family has various rituals and traditions.	___ 13. My family has few rituals and traditions.
___ 14. I do not take things that do not belong to me.	___ 14. I sometimes take things that do not belong to me.
___ TOTAL CHECK MARKS	___ TOTAL CHECK MARKS

*If you have more protective factors checked than risk factors, keep up the good work. If you have more risk factors checked than protective factors, you may want to seek counseling.

"IF I WERE ARRESTED"

Objective(s)

1. Students will predict what would happen in their lives if they were arrested for illegal drugs.

Materials

- Pencil
- *"If I Were Arrested" Worksheet*

Activity

1. Have the students fill out the *"If I Were Arrested" Worksheet*. After they have completed the worksheet, have them reflect on a personal level or share with classmates.

Educational Theme

- There are a wide variety of personal issues to face if you were arrested for illegal drugs.

"IF I WERE ARRESTED" WORKSHEET

Answer the following questions:

1. How would you feel if you were arrested for use or possession of illegal drugs?

2. What legal penalties might you face?

3. How would your parent(s) or guardian(s) feel?

4. Could this event affect your potential job future? How?

5. What is the overall message if you were arrested for illegal drugs?

"TEN THINGS YOU LIKE TO DO"

Objective(s)

1. Students will write ten things they like to do.

2. Students will decide if alcohol detracts from or enhances their favorite activities.

Materials Needed

- Paper and pencil

Activity

1. Ask students to list their ten favorite things to do.

2. Ask students to pick their top five from this list.

3. Tell students to look at their top five items. If alcohol would enhance that experience, put a "+" sign next to the item; if alcohol would detract from that activity, place a "-" sign by it.

4. Ask students how many had more "-" signs by their favorite activities than "+" signs. Use these answers for class discussion. (Previous use of this exercise indicates most students have "-" signs coinciding with their favorite things to do.)

Educational Theme

- There are many fun and exciting things to do without the use of alcohol and other drugs.

"THE FUTURE"

Objective(s)

1. Students will develop goals they want to reach in the future.

2. Students will see how alcohol and other drug abuse may interfere with their personal future goals.

Materials Needed

- Pencil and paper

Activity

1. Have students write down what they want to be doing five years and ten years from now.

2. Select students volunteer (or randomly pick some) to share their future goals.

3. Ask the students if alcohol or drug use could keep them from attaining <u>their</u> goals in life. Could getting busted for drugs interfere with a career in the military or other jobs?

Educational Theme

- Alcohol and other drug abuse can interfere with many areas in life, including career goals.

"THE PERFECT TOWN/CITY"

Objective(s)

1. Students will conceptualize (what it would be like in) the perfect town or city with no alcohol or other drug abuse.

Materials Needed

- Chalkboard or whiteboard, chalk or markers, and eraser

Activity

1. Tell the students to first think about what the perfect town or city with no alcohol or other drug abuse would be like. Have students take turns at the chalkboard to create such a place through drawing what their town or city would include.

2. Have students explain why they included their particular drawings.

Educational Theme

- Environmental factors (where we live, play, go to school, friends) all play an important role in the use or abuse of AOD.

Resources

1. Ashford, J., LeCroy, C. and Lortie, K. *Human Behavior in the Social Environment: A Multidimensional Perspective,* (3rd Ed.), Pacific Grove, CA: Brooks Cole, 2005.

"THE TOP TEN SONGS"

Objective(s)

1. Students will review the current top ten songs to analyze if sexuality or AOD use is portrayed.

Materials Needed

- Current top ten songs listing
- Tapes of top ten songs (may be required but students usually recognize these songs)
- Chalkboard or whiteboard, chalk or markers, and eraser

Activity

1. Present the list of the current top ten tunes to the students on the chalkboard. Go down each song and ask if it makes references to sex or AOD use. How many songs make reference to sex or AOD use? Ask, "What does that tell us about what sells in the record industry?"

Educational Theme

- The entertainment industry often uses references to sex or AOD to increase sales, profits and create attention.

Resources

1. Local music stores should have copies of current top ten songs.

"WELLNESS PUNCH GAME"

Objective(s)

1. Students will experience or see that negative behaviors can affect their health.
2. Students will understand that the more unhealthy behaviors you participate in, the risks to your overall health status also increases.

Materials Needed

- Business Cards (one per volunteer)
- Paper punch (one per volunteer)

Activity

1. Ask for two or three volunteers from the class. Tell them you are sending them down to earth and give each one a card representing their health. It's the only card they'll ever receive so they should take good care of it.
2. Read these health risk behaviors to the volunteers and have them punch their personal health cards.
   a. You use tobacco products on a regular basis. (Punch the card four times.)
   b. You drink to the point of forgetting what you do. (Punch the card four times.)
   c. You don't wear seat belts. (Punch the card four times.)
   d. You have taken steroids to gain an edge on the competition. (Punch the card four times.)
   e. You do not maintain the proper weight for your height. (Punch the card four times.)
   f. You do not get regular sleep?seven to eight hours per night. (Punch the card four times.)
   g. You become a couch potato and don't get regular physical activity. (Punch the card four times.)
   h. You don't eat breakfast daily. (Punch the card four times.)
   i. You don't eat three meals a day. (Punch the card four times.)
   j. You don't take time out to relieve stress in a healthy manner. (Punch the card four times.)
3. Have the volunteers hold up their personal health cards. Ask them what this experience means.

Educational Theme

- No one knows the extent risky behaviors and poor health habits influence our longevity.

Resources

1. Website <www.med.umich.edu> University of Michigan Health System.

"ADVICE COLUMN FOR SUBSTANCE ABUSE PREVENTION"

Objective(s)

1. Students will develop solutions to various substance abuse-related problems by composing responses to letters for an advice column.

Materials Needed

➢ Paper and pencils

➢ Letters for a fictitious advice column

Activity

1. Students will pretend that they have an advice column that appears in a newspaper.

2. Divide the class into groups giving each group a letter sent to the "advice column." They need to suggest solutions to the problem(s) presented in the letters by composing a response which would appear in a newspaper.

3. After the students have developed solutions and composed letters, have each group elect a spokesperson to read their advice letter to the class.

4. After each letter is read, discuss these solutions and ask if any other solutions are possible.

Educational Theme

➢ Many substance abuse problems exist in peoples' lives, but knowledge about these issues can lead to solutions.

Possible Letters to the Advice Column

Letter 1- I have been smoking marijuana on a regular basis. Can this lead to a serious problem? I thought marijuana was a safe drug.

Letter 2- When I drink alcohol my friends say I get wild and do stupid things. They do not want to hang out with me when I am drinking. Could this be a problem?

Letter 3- My friends are starting to use drugs. What can I do to not lose their friendship but not join in by using drugs with them?

Letter 4- Smokeless tobacco looks like a cool thing to do and you don't have to smoke. Are there any concerns I should have if I chose to use smokeless tobacco?

"COMPUTER ASSISTED LEARNING"

Objective(s)

1. Students will go on the Internet to find one web site regarding alcohol and other drug information to share with their classmates.

2. Students will gain knowledge of computers and information available on the Internet concerning alcohol and other drug prevention.

Materials Needed

➢ Computer equipment and internet access

Activity

1. As a class assignment students will team up in pairs and find information on alcohol and other drug prevention using the Internet. After they have found a site they will share the site address with their classmates and what types of information was available.

Educational Theme

➢ Students will gain knowledge of using computers and the Internet to access educational information.

Resources

1. Other learning activities in this book provide potential Internet websites for review.

"INFORMATION BROCHURE"

Objective(s)

1. Students will organize information about alcohol and other drugs into an informational brochure that they and others will easily be able to understand and use.

Materials Needed

- ➢ Computer equipment

Activity

1. Students will need to condense information about alcohol and other drugs of abuse into an informational brochure. The brochure may be designed in any format that their creative minds desire. This may be done individually or in small groups. The brochure must contain information about the substance, potential hazards of use, prevention of use and what treatment resources are available in the local community.

2. Once complete, display the various brochures around room so that students can observe and review the work of their peers.

Educational Theme

- ➢ Organizing and preparing information can be an effective learning method along with using students to educate other peers.

Resources

1. Collect a variety of education brochures that students can review in assisting them to design their class projects.

"MARINOL (DRONABINOL) AS MEDICINE"

Objective(s)

1. Students will observe how Marinol (active ingredient is THC) is used in modern medicine and that it has side effects just like smoking marijuana.

Materials Needed

- Worksheet provided (made into a transparency)
- Overhead projector

Activity

1. Have the students discuss the drugs Valium, Human Growth Hormone and Marinol as to how they are used in modern medicine and their side effects. As Marinol has side effects it does act as a real drug. Some students believe marijuana does nothing but get you high, then why is it used in medicine? The other two drugs can also be helpful and harmful.

Educational Theme

- Marijuana is a real drug and can be used in the practice of modern medicine, as with all drugs it has potential side effects.

Resources

1. Current copy of the "Physicians Desk Reference"

"DRUGS USED IN MODERN MEDICINE WORKSHEET"

Valium

Medical Uses

- Relief of tension and anxiety
- Can be used for acute alcohol withdrawal
- Relief of skeletal muscle spasm
- Spasticity from cerebral palsy
- Convulsive disorders-epilepsy
- Treat hallucinogen induced panic reactions
- Induce sleep

Side Effects

- Physical and psychological dependence
- Withdrawal upon abrupt discontinuance
- Dangerous when operating machinery, driving motor vehicles
- Dangerous to mix with alcohol or other depressants
- Increased risk of congenital malformations to fetus

Human Growth Hormone (HGH)

Medical Uses

- Used for growth deficient children
- May also preserve skin, boost immunity, improve heart and kidney function when used as an anti-aging hormone

Side Effects

- Grotesque facial features
- Swelling of the hand and feet
- Headaches, mood changes
- Visual disturbances
- Excessive sweating
- Offensive body odor
- Diabetes
- Death

Marinol (THC)

Medical Uses

- Appetite stimulant-AIDS patients
- Anti-nausea after chemotherapy when other conventional drugs have failed

Side Effects

- Feeling high
- Dizziness, confusion
- Danger to drive or operate machinery
- Dangerous for people with cardiovascular problems
- Substance abusers more prone to abuse this drug
- May compound effects of mental illness

"INVENT A LABEL"

Objective(s)

1. Students will create an educational alcoholic beverage label.

Materials Needed

- Paper, pencils, pens, markers, etc.

Activity

1. Remind students that all alcoholic products have labels with a health warning. Have each student create a product label of their own representing an issue related to alcohol abuse (i.e. "Drive My Car Drunk Beer" "Said Something Stupid Wine")

2. After students create their labels have them share with others or display in the classroom.

Educational Theme

- There are many potential hazards that can be involved with alcoholic beverages if misused.

"REACHING YOUR GOALS"

Objective(s)

1. Students will list their short term goals and how to achieve them.

2. Students will give examples of things that could keep them from reaching their goals.

Materials Needed

- Reaching Your Goals worksheet

- Pen or pencil

Activity

1. Have students fill out the worksheet Reaching Your Goals.

2. After students have complete their worksheets have them place in an envelop with their names on it.

3. After approximately a month return the envelops to the students to review and/or discuss in class. Questions could be Are they on track to reaching their goals? What things have helped or got in the way from reaching their goals? Should they revise their plans?

Educational Theme

- There are many things that can help you obtain your goals in life. You need to stay focused and make good decisions to accomplish goals.

REACHING YOUR GOALS WORKSHEET

Directions

Make a list of goals you think you can reach within a one month time span.

List of things you need to do to accomplish your goals.

Name things that could keep you from reaching your goals.

"PEER PRESSURE"

Objective(s)

1. Students will list ways other peers try to get them to use substances and ways to resist peer pressure.

2. Students will create examples of statements to help when they are under pressure to use substances.

Materials Needed

- Paper

- Pen or pencil

Activity

1. Have students form small groups.

2. Tell each group to write examples of things they have heard to get them to participate in risky situations. For each example have an answer to counter the pressure they are under.

3. Have the group's report back to the class and provide their examples.

Educational Theme

- There are many things can do to help you cope with peer pressure in avoiding high risk situations.

"DRUG ABUSE IN SPORTS"

Objective(s)

1. Students will discuss athletes who were busted using performance enhancing drugs to gain an edge in sports.

2. Students will describe the consequences these athletes faced from their decisions to use drugs.

Materials Needed

➢ Chalkboard or whiteboard, eraser, and chalk or makers

Activity

1. Discuss with students famous athletes that have been busted for using performance enhancing drugs (Marion Jones-Track and Field, Manny Ramirez-Baseball, Kelli White-Track and Field, Floyd Landis-Cycling etc.).

2. Ask students to describe how using performance enhancing drugs has affected the careers of these and other individuals. Put the information on the board as students provide answers to this question for continued discussion.

Educational Theme

➢ There is a big price to pay for using performance enhancing drugs.

Resources

1. Internet search for athletes busted for use of performance enhancing drugs.

"BASEBALL"

Objective(s)

1. Students will identify how making good choice can help you succeed.

Materials Needed

- Chalkboard or whiteboard, eraser, chalk or markers
- Small pieces of paper, scissors and ink pen

Activity

1. The instructor will design a baseball field on the chalkboard or whiteboard. Cut small pieces of paper with the following choices:
   -Stay at a party where drugs are at "strike out"
   -Go to a party and you see underage drinkers so you leave "base hit"
   -Invited to a party but you know there may be trouble there so you don't go "home run"
   -Get into a fight or argument at a party "fly out"
   -Plan activity with your friends that is substance free "base hit"
   -A friend offers you a drug and you say no thanks "base hit"
   -Do something you regret while drinking or drunk "strike out"

2. Split the class into two teams. Have students select one piece of paper (folded so can't see the answer) at a time and read. The instructor will track the progress of the baseball game on the board so students can see results of their actions. Play at least one inning and see which team wins.

Educational Theme

- Students will see how making good decisions can lead to positive outcomes through playing a game.

"JUST SAY YES TOO?"

Objective(s)

1. Students will select options to using alcohol and other drugs of abuse.

2. Students will state alternatives to alcohol and other drugs of abuse.

Materials Needed

- None

Activity

1. Students will think of and select alternatives to alcohol and other drug abuse to share with their classmates (i.e. playing their sport of choice, going to the movies, playing video games with friends).

2. Students will take turns saying "I will say yes too _____. Have all students participate.

Educational Theme

- Students will get ideas to help avoid using alcohol and other drugs by hearing about fun activities they can select that their peers also enjoy.

Resources

1. None needed

"BODY, MIND, SPIRIT"

Objective(s)

1. Students will develop a list to describe how drugs can affect your body, mind and spirit.

2. Students will report to class the team findings.

Materials Needed

- ➢ Computer
- ➢ Internet
- ➢ Library resources

Activity

1. Divide the students into teams. Each team will select a drug of interest to research how the chemical affects the body, mind and spirit of individuals using this drug.

2. Students will develop a one page (or more) typed report on their findings to present to class.

Educational Theme

- ➢ Drug use and abuse can affect the body, mind and spirit of the individual using the substance.

Resources

1. Internet and local library resources

"POSITIVE WAYS TO HANDLE STRESS"

Objective(s)

1. Students will list positive ways to handle stress in their lives.

Materials Needed

- Positive Ways To Handle Stress Worksheet (see following page)
- Pen or pencil

Activity

1. People often handle stressful feelings and emotions by using alcohol and other drugs to blunt their affect. This can lead to negative outcomes and the feelings are still not dealt with. This method of dealing with stress over a period of time can lead to addiction or problems with these substances.
2. Have the students complete the "Positive Ways To Handle Stress" worksheet. This will give them coping strategies they can incorporate into their lives.
3. You may want to have students share their lists with classmates.

Educational Theme

- There are many ways to deal with stress in our lives without resorting to alcohol and other drug abuse.

POSITIVE WAYS TO HANDLE STRESS WORKSHEET

- Develop a list of positive ways you can deal with stress in your life.

"INTERNET RESEARCH"

Objective(s)

1. Students will complete the worksheet Internet Research to learn more about a drug of interest.

Materials Needed

- Internet Research worksheet
- Pen or pencil
- Computer with internet access

Activity

1. Have each student fill out the worksheet Internet Research.
2. After students have completed their worksheets they can share their findings with fellow classmates.

Educational Theme

- Individuals can do their own research to learn new information about any substance of interest.

Resources

1. Internet

"INTERNET RESEARCH WORKSHEET"

Student name:

Drug chosen to research:

How is the substance taken?

Side effects from using this drug?

How long due the effects last?

What is the drug used for?

Is this drug legal or illegal to use?

How is the drug produced?

What new information did you learn about this substance?

References used:

"DOES YOUR PERCEPTION BECOME YOUR REALITY?"

Objective(s)

1. Students will answer how perceptions can become their reality in dealing with tobacco and other drug use.

2. Students will summarize how peers affect their outlook on use rates of tobacco and other drugs.

Materials Needed

- Pictures of illusions from the internet

- Overhead project and screen

Activity

1. Show pictures of illusions found on the internet to the students in class. While doing this activity ask the students what they see? Students will soon see how their perceptions become how they view reality.

2. Knowing this information the teacher can discuss how deviant behavior stands out in a crowd. One example is students may believe a large number of people smoke cigarettes when in reality it is less than 30% of adults in the United States. If their perception is most or many people smoke they may be more enticed to try tobacco products. This example shows how perceptions can distort reality just like the illusions that were shown in class.

Educational Theme

- One's perception can have a very large impact on how you view reality and the environment you live in.

Resources

- Internet search of illusions

PART II

HIV/AIDS AND STD'S

"CULTURAL/AGE GROUP SPECIFIC HIV/AIDS EDUCATION"

Objective(s)

1. Students will develop cultural/age group specific HIV/AIDS education methods.

2. Students will demonstrate that HIV/AIDS education methods should be culturally or age group specific.

Materials Needed

➢ None

Activity

1. Ask the students to share their impressions on how an effective HIV/AIDS education program would reach people their own age or cultural background. After students see these examples, break students into small groups to design cultural or age specific methods to provide information about HIV/AIDS.

2. Have student groups report back to the larger group. Create a list of these methods for everyone to see and discuss. Are there similarities, differences?

Educational ➢Theme

➢ HIV/AIDS educational methods should be culturally/age group specific.

Resources

1. Stall, R. and Mills, T. "A Quarter Century of AIDS," *Amer. J. Public Health*, 96 (2006):959.

"FACTS IN MOTION"

Objective(s)

1. Students will state current facts about HIV/AIDS and follow these facts by some body motion.

Materials Needed

- ➢ List of current facts about HIV/AIDS with movement statement following.

Activity

1. Prepare a list of current HIV/AIDS facts followed by a movement statement (i.e., Fact: AIDS is caused by the Human Immunodeficiency Virus, Motion: Fall Down/Fact: HIV can be spread through blood, semen and body fluids, motion: Stand on a chair.).

2. Ask students to read these facts and then follow them by the action statement. This can be a fun way to review test questions.

Educational Theme

- ➢ Cognitive information can be reinforced by follow-up action.

Resources

1. Website <www.cdc.gov/hiv/ > Centers for Disease Control and Prevention.

"HIV POSITIVE GUEST SPEAKER"

Objective(s)

1. Students will meet someone face to face who is HIV positive or is diagnosed with AIDS.

Materials Needed

- None

Activity

1. Invite a guest speaker that is HIV positive. Through contact with your local Health Department, hospital health education unit, or other health agency, you should be able to find a guest speaker that is HIV positive. Try to find someone that is close to the age of the group they are speaking to. (Some research is indicating this is an effective approach to HIV/AIDS education.)

Educational Theme

- Using real people/peers who are HIV positive create a powerful message concerning HIV/AIDS prevention.

Resources

1. Website <www.apla.org/> AIDS Project Los Angeles.

"HIV/AIDS AND PHYSICS"

Objective(s)

1. Students will view the process of transmission of HIV/AIDS and other STDs as random and learn that risk factors are variable due to the nature of science.

Materials Needed

- Deck of playing cards

Activity

1. Take the deck of playing cards and drop them on the floor in front of the students. Keep repeating this sequence while asking the students what you are doing and how this relates to HIV/AIDS and other STDs. Science acts in random order. Just as the playing cards fall in a random pattern, even if you are exposed to a particular virus or other disease-causing organism, you may not develop or contract the disease.

Educational Theme

- Based on physics science acts in random order and everyone exposed to HIV or other STD's may not become infected.

Resources

1. Hawkings, S., *A Brief History of Time*. New York: Bantam Books. 1988.

2. Pirsig, R. M. *Zen and the Act of Motorcycle Maintenance*. New York: Bantam Books. 1974.

"HIV/AIDS HIGH RISK GROUPS"

Objective(s)

1. Students will view how the history of HIV/AIDS is changing for high risk groups.

2. Students will recognize that as high risk groups are changing, anyone can put themselves at risk for HIV/AIDS.

Materials Needed

➢ Chalkboard or whiteboard, chalk or markers, and eraser

Activity

1. Write on the chalkboard: "Factors contributing to HIV/AIDS High Risk Groups," adding one at a time. Ask students to pay attention. After each factor, state, "I forgot one." (List should include:)

   ➢ Gay Males
   ➢ IV Drug Users
   ➢ Hemophiliac
   ➢ People of Color
   ➢ Women
   ➢ Teens
   ➢ Anybody

2. Ask the students how this list reflects the history of the HIV/AIDS epidemic in the U.S. Other questions to ask include, "Is HIV/AIDS restricted to any particular group of people?" "What is more important, your behavior or the group you may belong to?"

Educational Theme

➢ There is no longer a high risk group for contracting HIV/AIDS. It can infect anyone.

Resources

1. Website <www.nejm.org> New England Journal of Medicine.

"HOW TO AVOID HIV RISK SITUATIONS"

Objective(s)

1. Students will understand, develop, and explain how to avoid becoming infected with HIV.

Materials Needed

➢ Paper and pencils

Activity

1. Share that having unprotected sex and sharing needles after IV drug use are high risk situations for acquiring HIV. Ask the students to develop their own lists of how to avoid these risky situations.

2. Have students break into small groups and share their ideas with other classmates.

Educational Theme

➢ Risk factors for becoming infected with HIV are related to behaviors, as opposed to disease.

Resources

1. Website <www.safersex.org>

"IS THIS SAFE?"

Objective(s)

1. Students will determine what actions are high risk behavior in relation to HIV/AIDS.

Materials Needed

- Poster board
- Magic markers

Activity

1. Draw a variety of examples of safe and high risk behaviors related to HIV/AIDS on poster board (example: Toilet seat, IV drug needle, lips/kissing, etc.).
2. Hold up your posters, one at a time, have students give a thumbs up for safe behaviors and a thumbs down for high risk behaviors. Then give the correct answers after each example is shown to the class.

Educational Theme

- It is sometimes difficult to know what might be a high risk behavior for acquiring an HIV infection.

Resources

1. Donatelle, R.J. *Access to Health,* (9th Ed.), San Francisco: Pearson Benjamin Cummings, 2006.

"MATCH THE ANSWER"

Objective(s)

1. Students will match questions and answers on information concerning HIV/AIDS.

2. Students will review test questions by matching questions and answers.

Materials Needed

- 3" × 5" note cards
- Answer sheet (for instructor)

Activity

1. The instructor will develop question and answer cards on separate 3" × 5" note cards.

2. The question note cards are placed on a table in one part of the room and the answer cards on another table. Students will pick up a question card then try to match it with an answer card. When all cards have been collected, the teacher will read the answers. (If one or more individuals select an incorrect card, all the cards will not match.)

Educational Theme

- Reviewing for tests can be done in an entertaining fashion.

"PREDICT THE FUTURE OF HIV/AIDS"

Objective(s)

1. Students will predict future trends or discoveries in relation to the HIV/AIDS pandemic.

Materials Needed

- *Crystal Ball Worksheet* (one per student, see the following page)
- Pencil

Activity

1. Have students predict the future trends and discoveries in relation to the HIV/AIDS epidemic by using the "Crystal Ball Worksheet."
2. Complete the exercise and have students read some of their predictions to the class for discussion.

Educational Theme

- No one knows the future trends or discoveries concerning the HIV/AIDS pandemic.

Resources

1. Kuhn, T. S. *The Structure of Scientific Revolutions*, (2nd Ed.), Chicago: University of Chicago Press, 1970.

CRYSTAL BALL WORKSHEET

Instructions: Write your predictions for future trends and discoveries concerning HIV/AIDS inside the crystal ball.

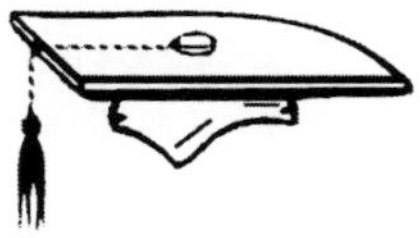

"RESEARCHING HIV/AIDS"

Objective(s)

1. Students will review various literature concerning HIV/AIDS.

2. Students will report on their research findings on HIV/AIDS.

Materials Needed

- Scientific journals, books, magazines
- *Researching HIV/AIDS Worksheet* (see following page)

Activity

1. Have students, as a homework assignment, research HIV/AIDS using the worksheet format provided. Skip the worksheet format sections that may not apply to the article being reviewed. The HIV/AIDS epidemic literature changes and is updated on a daily basis, students should have no difficulty finding articles to review.

2. Upon completion of the assignment, have students report back their findings.

Educational Theme

- There is currently a wide variety of literature and research concerning issues related to HIV/AIDS.

Resources

1. Scientific journals, books, magazines.

"RESEARCHING HIV/AIDS WORKSHEET"

Source/Reference of Your Article:

Purpose of the Article:

Population or Target Group Studied:

General Findings:

Summary/Your Impressions of the Research Completed:

"TAKING ACTION TO PREVENT HIV/AIDS"

Objective(s)

1. Students will list a variety of actions that can prevent the contraction of HIV/AIDS.

Materials Needed

- *Taking Action to Prevent HIV/AIDS Worksheet* (see following page)
- Pencil

Activity

1. Explain that HIV is a weak virus, it requires the right conditions to infect people through blood, semen, or other body fluids. With what we now know about HIV, people usually have to put themselves at risk to become HIV positive.

2. Have students complete the worksheet, "Taking Action to Prevent HIV/AIDS" and then discuss it with fellow classmates.

Educational Theme

- We have a vaccine for HIV/AIDS—it's called education. People often place themselves at risk for contracting HIV/AIDS.

Resources

1. Website <www.vitae.org/vitae/aids/condoms.html>.

"TAKING ACTION TO PREVENT HIV/AIDS WORKSHEET"

Instructions: Complete the worksheet by describing ways you can place yourself at risk for contracting HIV.

1.

2.

3.

4.

5.

6.

7.

8.

9.

10.

"THE BODY BAG"

Objective(s)

1. Students will view and examine a body bag.

2. Students will encounter what may happen from the long term consequences of HIV disease or AIDS.

Materials Needed

- One body bag (may be obtained from a local hospital or undertaker)

Activity

1. Explain that HIV disease or AIDS is considered a fatal disease and although we can treat the disease, it is totally preventable.

2. Pass the body bag around the class or if someone volunteers, zip them partially up in the bag. Some people believe condoms are too confining, ask the class how confining they think a body bag would be.

Educational Theme

- Having unprotected sex can have extreme consequences including death.

Designed by M. H. "Mark" Jones.

"TOO HOT TO HANDLE"

Objective(s)

1. Students will learn that not every high risk contact with HIV will cause infection.

Materials Needed

➢ "Electronic Hot Potato Game"

Activity

1. Take out the potato from the game "Electronic Hot Potato Game." (The potato has a musical timer in it.)

2. Have the students stand up in class and give one person the potato. Start the musical timer and have the students toss it around the class as the music plays. As the music stops, have those individuals holding the potato sit down. You can do this a few times.

3. Explain that although many people have unprotected sex (the potato), you may not become infected. Risk factors are like the potato and can sometimes be handled without paying the price, sometimes not. Some people play these games many times without consequences; others are not as fortunate.

Educational Theme

➢ Unprotected sex is risky. You never know when you might contract HIV or another STD.

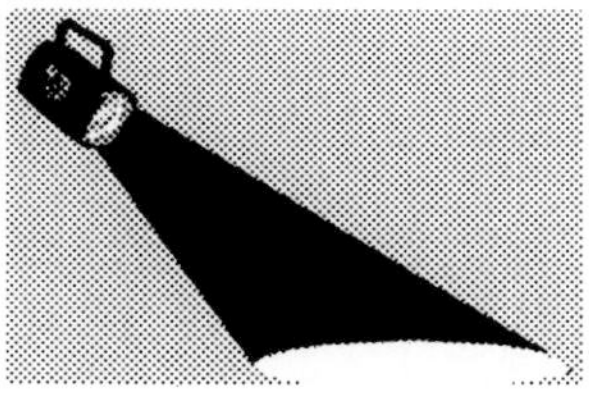

"WHAT'S NEW ON FILM?"

Objective(s)

1. Students will view, select, and present current HIV/AIDS information from a film of their choice.

2. Students will share with other classmates why they believe their film would be effective in HIV/AIDS education.

Materials Needed

- Film on HIV/AIDS

- VCR or DVD and monitor

Activity

1. Break students up into small groups to view, select, and present an HIV/AIDS education film of their choice. Current films or videos can usually be obtained from their school media library, local health department, university/college media center, etc.

2. Ask, after the video is presented, each group to explain why they believe their video would be effective in the fight against HIV/AIDS. Each group should be open to defend their comments and choice of educational materials.

Educational Theme

- Peers may be the best judge of what is effective for HIV/AIDS education.

Resources

1. Various film catalogs, local and state library media collections.

"CRITTERS THAT GROW ON YOU"

Objective(s)

1. Students will learn of the variety of STDs that they can become infected with.

Materials Needed

- Poster board
- Magic markers

Activity

1. Have the students create a critter that represents an STD. After they have created their critter, have each student present a fact about the STD along with the artwork.

Educational Theme

- There are a variety of STDs that are very common and people need to protect themselves against these diseases.

Resources

1. Website <www.ashastd.org/std/std.html>

"ONE IN FIVE"

Objective(s)

1. Students will perceive the high probability of contracting an STD in their lifetime.

Materials Needed

➢ None

Activity

1. Have the students count off from one to five, then have all the number fives stand up (or raise their hands). Explain that their chances of acquiring an STD sometime in their lifetime is approximately 20 percent.

2. Ask the students either sitting or standing to state how they feel about their risk potential for STDs. Are they really at risk? How do they feel about these odds for acquiring an STD?

Educational Theme

➢ STDs are very common and protecting yourself should always be kept in mind.

Resources

1. U.S. Department of Health and Human Services, *Healthy People 2010, National Health Promotion and Disease Prevention Objectives*. Public Health Service.

"PICK A BALLOON"

Objective(s)

1. Students will state how multiple sexual relationships can increase their risk of acquiring an STD.

Materials Needed

- 15 Balloons
- Small pieces of paper placed in balloons

Activity

1. Write down the name of an STD on one in every five pieces of paper. Place the pieces, one piece per balloon, then inflate balloons.

2. Have students pick balloons to represent multiple sexual relationships. Now break each balloon to see if there is a chance of contracting an STD from your partner. Help the students explain the answers (STD they may have contracted) and discuss the risks of multiple sexual partners.

Educational Theme

- Multiple sexual relationships and not using safer sex methods can increase your risk of acquiring an STD.

"STD MOBILE"

Objective(s)

1. Students will construct an STD mobile.

2. Students will define various STDs.

Materials Needed

- Poster board
- String or fish line
- Magic markers
- Clothes hangers

Activity

1. Discuss with students various STDs, then have the students construct an STD mobile featuring a variety of STDs. Students can make funny-looking bugs to represent the STDs on their mobile.

2. Ask students to share the mobiles with their classmates along with re-enforcing information about STDs.

Educational Theme

- There are a variety of STD's and creative ways to learn about them.

Resources

1. Grimes, J. *Seductive Delusions: How Everyday People Catch STDs*, Baltimore: Johns Hopkins University Press, 2008.

"UGLIFY AN STD"

Objective(s)

1. Students will design posters and explain an STD's signs and symptoms.

Materials Needed

- Poster board and magic markers
- Information on STDs, fact sheets, etc.

Activity

1. Have students break into small groups to uglify and explain an STD. Groups are asked to draw a cartoon version of the STD provided by the facilitator and explain its signs and symptoms.
2. Ask all groups, upon completion of their posters and research, to report back to the entire class.

Educational Theme

- STDs are not a pretty sight and have a wide variety of signs and symptoms.

Resources

1. Hyde, J. and DeLamater, J. *Understanding Human Sexuality*, (10th Ed.), Boston: McGraw-Hill, 2007.

"CONDOM SIZE"

Objective(s)

1. Students will examine the physical properties of latex condoms.

Materials Needed

➢ Latex condoms

Activity

1. Show students how much stress a latex condom can withstand, or that one size fits all. Stretch the condom over a shoe, hand, or multiple fingers. The rim of the condom may have to be stretched in order to accommodate a large object.

Educational Theme

➢ Latex condoms can accommodate many shapes and sizes.

Resources

1. Website <www.planned parenthood.org/birth-control/contrachoices.htm>.

"DON'T USE AN OIL-BASED LUBRICANT"

Objective(s)

1. Students will review why oil-based lubricants should not be used on latex condoms.

Materials Needed

- Latex Condoms
- Vaseline Petroleum Jelly

Activity

1. Explain to students that oil-based lubricants should not be used with latex condoms. Blow up or inflate a condom with oxygen, sealing in the air. Now have a student rub Vaseline Petroleum Jelly on the condom (keep the condom away from your face and at arms length.) The condom should break, which will visually demonstrate the property being explained.

Educational Theme

- Oil-based lubricants break down latex and should not be used on condoms.

"NINE STEPS TO CONDOM USE"

Objective(s)

1. Students will learn how to use a condom correctly.

Materials Needed

- ➢ Nine pieces of poster board
- ➢ Magic markers

Activity

1. Prepare each poster board with a step of correct condom use. The steps are listed below:
   a. Become aroused (penis is erect).
   b. Discuss condom use with your partner.
   c. Open the condom package carefully so you don't tear the condom or make a hole in the condom with your fingernail.
   d. Take hold of ½ inch at the tip of the condom and roll the condom down to the base of the penis.
   e. Gently smooth out any air bubbles.
   f. Ejaculate.
   g. Hold the condom at the base of the penis while pulling out so that the condom doesn't leak or fall off.
   h. Roll the condom off starting at the base of the penis.
   i. Throw the condom away in the garbage.
2. Ask for nine student volunteers. Each person will take a poster board and stand in front of the group. The volunteers cannot talk. The rest of the students will instruct the student volunteers where each person should stand. The activity ends when the steps are in order.

Educational Theme

- ➢ For maximum effectiveness in promoting safer sex, condoms have to be used consistently and correctly.

Designed by Matt Calfin

"THE CONDOM RELAY RACE"

Objective(s)

1. Male students will begin to develop the ability to feel comfortable touching condoms.

2. Students will learn that putting on a condom takes little time and effort.

Materials Needed

- Thirty condoms

- Masking tape

Activity

1. Ask for twelve student volunteers. Split the volunteers into groups of two. The six groups will stand approximately 15 feet across from each other. Use masking tape to designate where each member of the group is to stand. One student from each group will stand with fingers "erect" pointing toward their partner. Instruct the groups that the first group finished putting the condoms on their partner's fingers is the winner.

Educational Theme

- Using a condom takes little time and effort.

Designed by Matt Calfin.

"TIME THAT CONDOM"

Objective(s)

1. Students will see that the use of a condom to promote safer sex (if you are sexually active) only requires a few seconds.

2. Students will view that the use of condoms is not very difficult.

Materials Needed

- Latex condom
- Two volunteers
- Watch with second hand

Activity

1. Ask for two volunteers from the class to take part in this game or demonstration. Have them face each other approximately five feet apart. One of the volunteers will point two fingers straight out, the other will receive the condom. Ask the volunteer with the condom to place it on the others fingers as quickly as possible while the instructor times this event. This usually requires only 10 to 30 seconds to complete. The instructor can say that if you are sexually active, these seconds could save your life or a lot of future problems from contracting STDs. Some people complain that it takes too long to use a condom, this experiment should prove otherwise.

Educational Theme

- If you're sexually active, using a condom takes little effort and can save your life or a lot of future problems.

"CREATE YOUR OWN LEARNING STRATEGY"

Objective(s)

1. Students will create their own active learning method (can be used for any health-related topic).

Materials Needed

- Will be presented or described by the student.

Activity

1. Provide some examples of active learning techniques. Challenge the students to design and present their own. This can become part of a report on a health topic and can be done in teams if students are too anxious or embarrassed to present on their own.

Educational Theme

- Peer education methodologies can be an effective approach in health promotion/disease prevention.

Resources

1. Various internet websites, books, magazines, journals, etc.

"GUESS THE TERM"

Objective(s)

1. Students will become familiar with birth control and human sexuality terms.

2. Students will identify a variety of birth control methods and human body parts.

Materials Needed

- 3" × 5" note cards with various birth control and or human sexuality terms written on one side of the card.

- Chalk and eraser.

- Chalkboard or whiteboard, chalk or markers, and eraser, or large writing tablet with a marker.

Activity

1. Select a volunteer from the classroom and only show him/her the card (term) you are holding.

2. Ask student to draw, without speaking, a facsimile of the term on the chalkboard while other students in the class guess out loud what the term is. The first student to guess correctly comes up to draw the next picture from the cards. This can be a good review of human sexuality terms and help to make students feel more comfortable discussing these topics and issues.

Educational Theme

- Using human sexuality terms in a game can help people feel more comfortable discussing these topics.

Resources

1. Phillips, C. *Socrates Cafe*, New York: W.W. Norton and Company, 2001.

"I FAILED TO MENTION . . ."

Objective(s)

1. Students will see that sometimes people don't tell much about their past sexual relationships.

2. Students will witness that one sexual contact may actually be related to many.

Materials Needed

➢ None

Activity

1. Ask for eight volunteers from your classroom or group. Start with two people standing side by side and state that they had been dating and finally had a sexual relationship.

2. State that one partner failed to mention having a relationship with "X." ("X" joins the group.) After this, the other student said he didn't mention he had a short relationship with "XX." Then "X" states he had a relationship with "XXX." As each name is mentioned, they join the group. Soon it is easy to visualize; how many people can be involved in this situation or transfer of an STD.

Educational Theme

➢ When you have sex with someone, you come in contact with everyone they have had sex with previously.

Resources

1. Crooks, R.L. *Our Sexuality*. (10th Ed.), Florence, Ky: Wadsworth Publishing, 2007.

"JUST SAY NO TO SEX"

Objective(s)

1. Students will practice saying no to sex.

Materials Needed

- None

Activity

1. Ask students one at a time (by going around the room), how they would say no to sex in a tense situation. Remember to tell the students they can pass if they feel uncomfortable about this activity.

2. Repeat some of the best responses for the students to remember. Tell the students that no means no and that date rape is a crime.

Educational Theme

- Date rape is a crime and no always means no.

Resources

1. Hamilton, J. *Date Rape: Issues that Concern You*, Farmington Hills, MI: Greenhaven Press, 2007.

"SAFER SEX WHILE INTOXICATED?"

Objective(s)

1. Students will demonstrate how coordination would be affected if intoxicated.

Materials Needed

- Latex Condom

Activity

1. Select two volunteers from the class. Have one student place two fingers out straight. Give the condom to the other volunteer.

2. Tell the student with the condom to take it out of the package (using the non-dominate hand during the entire process) and place it over the other students fingers.

3. Ask the student (that put the condom on) if it was more difficult than it would have been using their dominate hand. Could this be similar to being intoxicated and trying to use a condom correctly? What else could happen if intoxicated? (Date rape, unplanned pregnancies, becoming infected with an STD.)

Educational Theme

- Being intoxicated impairs coordination, judgement, and sometimes memory.

Resources

1. Fields, R. *Drugs in Perspective: Causes, Assessment, Family, Prevention, Intervention and Treatment*, (7th Ed.), Boston: McGraw-Hill, 2010.

"SEX POSTERS"

Objective(s)

1. Students will create a poster depicting how media portrays human sexuality.

2. Students will learn some of the advertizing techniques in promoting products related to sexuality.

Materials Needed

- Poster Board
- Glue
- Various magazines and newspapers

Activity

1. Have the students develop a poster from clippings from magazines and newspapers with advertisements dealing with issues related to human sexuality (i.e., movies, clothing, dating, wedding rings, etc.).

2. Have the students, upon completion of the project, explain their poster and what it means to them. What kinds of societal peer pressure do these concepts create? What are some of the major themes that persist with these advertisements?

Educational Theme

- The media uses human sexuality in a variety of formats to promote various products, movies, clothing, etc.

Resources

1. Various magazines and newspapers.

"SEXOPOLY"

Objective(s)

1. Students will view how random consequences can occur when having unprotected sex with someone.

Materials Needed

- Poster board
- Magic markers
- Magazines

Activity

1. Design a Sexopoly Board with the front composed of various individuals and sexes taken from magazines. Place a number under each individual picture. On the back side, place your numbers across the top and the alphabet on the side.

   Example:

	1	2	3	4	5	6
A						
B						

2. Place various consequences in each block on the back side example: HIV+, Warts, Guilt, Had Good Time.
3. Give students the opportunity to pick individuals on the front side, people they might want to have sex with (without telling others in the class who they selected).
4. Turn the board over and have them match up their number(s) with their first letter of their last name to see what may have randomly taken place.
5. Ask students to discuss their findings or just keep it a personal experience.

Educational Theme

- Sexual relationships can have both positive and negative outcomes, so if you are sexually active, you should always use a latex condom.

Designed by: Jason Laker

"SEXUAL RELATIONS CAN HAVE MANY CONSEQUENCES"

Objective(s)

1. Students will experience how personal choices in sexual relationships can lead to a variety of outcomes or consequences.
2. Students will view the randomness of potential consequences.

Materials Needed

- Plastic sandwich bags (enough for each student)
- Pieces of candy or peanuts (enough for each student)
- After you place the candy or peanuts in the plastic bags, tie them with either a red, white, blue or green ribbons.

Activity

1. Hand out the filled bags to all students in the classroom. Tell the students they can do what they want with the bags.
2. Give a lecture or talk for a while.
3. Tell the students what the different colored ribbons stand for:

White Ribbon:	Your sexual partner was free of all STDs, including HIV.
Red Ribbon:	Your sexual partner was HIV positive.
Blue Ribbon:	Your sexual partner has active herpes.
Green Ribbon:	Your sexual partner has human pap virus (HPV) or warts.

Educational Theme

- Sexual relations can have many consequences and these consequences are random in nature.

Resources

1. Scholly, K., *et al*. "Using Social Norms Theory to Explain Perceptions and Sexual Health Behaviors of Undergraduate College Students: An Exploratory Study," *J Am College Health*, 53 (2005): 159-166.

"TOO MUCH SEX ON TV"

Objective(s)

1. Students will review television shows that use issues related to human sexuality to gain a viewing audience.

2. Students will rate television shows as to low, medium, high, or no sexual connotations used in the programming.

Materials Needed

- TV Guide

- Chalkboard or whiteboard, chalk or markers, and eraser

Activity

1. Break students into small discussion groups and give each group the evening programming section from the TV Guide.

2. Ask the groups to rate television shows, using human sexuality issues to gain viewer audience as low, medium, high, or no sexual connotations.

3. Ask the small groups to report back to the class as a whole. Keep track on the chalkboard of the overall ratings. What are the results? Is television using sexual cues frequently? Are these some of the more popular shows? What messages does it send our society?

Educational Theme

- Television and other media often use human sexuality to gain a viewing audience.

Resources

1. *TV Guide*.

"UNIVERSAL PRECAUTIONS EQUIPMENT"

Objective(s)

1. Students will learn about a variety of universal precautions devices and equipment.

2. Students will realize the seriousness of bloodborne pathogens by use of safety equipment.

Materials Needed

- A variety of devices and equipment currently in use for protection from bloodborne pathogens (i.e., latex gloves, masks, face shields, disposable gowns, sharpes containers, etc.)

Activity

1. Have a medical personnel explain and show a variety of universal precautions equipment to your class. Discuss how this has changed the medical profession in recent years.

Educational Theme

- Universal precautions devices and equipment are currently very common in the workplace setting and can prevent disease and illness.

Resources

1. Local American Red Cross office or Health Department

"WHY ABSTINENCE IS COOL"

Objective(s)

1. Students will explain why they believe abstinence is "cool."

Materials Needed

- Paper and pencils
- Large pad of paper

Activity

1. Have each student list on a piece of paper why they believe abstinence is "cool." Tell them not to put their names on the papers because you will collect them to make a composite listing.
2. Collect the student statements and make a listing of these on a large sheet of paper. These statements can then be shared and discussed in class and placed on a bulletin board for further review and thought.

Educational Theme

- You won't acquire HIV/AIDS or STD's by abstaining from sexual intercourse. Everyone is not "doing it."

"WRITE YOUR OWN PUBLIC SERVICE ANNOUNCEMENTS"

Objective(s)

1. Students will write and perform their own PSA for radio or television.

Materials Needed

- Paper and pencil

Activity

1. Explain how PSAs are utilized and provide an example to the students so they can see how they are written.

2. Have the students create their own PSA (concerning prevention of HIV/AIDS) for TV or radio. Then have them present the PSA to their classmates. Try to keep the PSA to within one minute air time.

EXAMPLE PSAS

1. Important Fact, you cannot get HIV/AIDS by donating blood! This message was brought to you by the Isabella County Drug Prevention Council, Mason Substance Abuse Services, and your local police department. (15-Second Spot)

2. Abstinence is 100 percent effective in preventing HIV/AIDS and other sexually transmitted diseases. If you are sexually active, stay healthy, and always use a latex condom. This message was brought to you by the Isabella County Drug Prevention Council and the Mason Substance Abuse Services. (15-Second Spot)

Educational Theme

- PSA's can reach a large amount of people with minimal time invested.

"LETTER TO THE EDITOR"

Objective(s)

1. Students will record their feelings about HIV/AIDS in a "Letter to the Editor."

Materials

- Paper and pencils
- Bulletin Board

Activity

1. Have the students imagine (or this may be a real situation) that a relative or friend is dying from HIV/AIDS.
2. Have each student write a mock "Letter to the Editor" that would describe their feelings if this were a real situation. What would they tell the public? How does HIV/AIDS affect their lives?

Educational Theme

- Living or knowing someone with HIV/AIDS can be very emotional and/or difficult.

"EXCUSES, EXCUSES"

Objective(s)

1. Students will identify "excuses" that individuals have for not using condoms during sexual relations and will develop solutions for these risky behaviors.

Materials Needed

- ➢- Paper and pencils
- ➢ Chalkboard or whiteboard, chalk or markers, and eraser

Activity

1. Place the following HIV/AIDS prevention method on the chalkboard: "Avoid exchange of body fluids by using condoms during sexual relations"
2. Ask students to identify and make a list of "excuses" people may give for <u>not</u> using this proven barrier device.
3. Have students write on the chalkboard their favorite "excuse" they believe people use.
4. After all the "excuses" have been listed on the chalkboard, have the students rate their top five.
5. For the top five "excuses" listed, develop solutions by getting student feedback and place on the chalkboard for discussion.

Educational Theme

➢ People may have "excuses" for placing themselves at risk for contracting HIV/AIDS, but there are solutions for these dangerous "excuses."

Resources

1. Zinn-Kabat, J. *Wherever You Go There You Are*, New York: Hyperion, 1994.

"A - Z ABOUT HIV/AIDS"

Objective(s)

1. Students will identify words associated with HIV/AIDS

Materials Needed

- Paper, pencils and dictionaries

Activity

1. Students will identify a word associated with HIV/AIDS for every letter of the alphabet (a = acquired, b = blood, etc.).

Educational Theme

- Information about HIV/AIDS covers a wide vocabulary maybe the entire alphabet, this is your chance to discover if it does.

Resources

1. Website <www.awesomelibrary.org/> library resources

2. Website <www.cdc.gov/diseasesconditions/>HIV and STD information

"THUMBS UP/DOWN ABOUT AIDS"

Objective(s)

1. Students will differentiate between common facts and myths about HIV/AIDS.

Materials Needed

- Paper and Pencils

Activity

1. Students are asked to write down three things they have heard about HIV/AIDS on a sheet of paper.

2. Once papers are collected by the instructor, each statement is read to the entire class. As each statement is read, all students will be asked to put their thumbs up if they think the statement is factual, down if they think the statement is false. This allows for both discussion and debate on the statements to provide a clear understanding of issues the students have been exposed too.

Educational Theme

- Factual information about HIV/AIDS is important in understanding this disease, yet many misleading statements may exist.

Resources

1. Website <www.cdc.gov/hiv/> HIV/AIDS information from CDC

"CARTOONS CAN TEACH"

Objective(s)

1. Students will design a cartoon with a minimum of four frames explaining a myth about HIV/AIDS.

Materials Needed

- Paper, rulers, colored pencils/markers

Activity

1. Following class discussions on facts and myths about HIV/AIDS, students will be asked to think about a cartoon they enjoy on TV or in the movies. As cartoons often make a statement about life, so will the ones the students will design.

2. Explain that each students will be a cartoonist for the day (don't worry about drawing quality as it is the message that is most important). They will need to draw four or more frames to develop their idea and later present to their classmates.

Educational Theme

- While cartoons are fun they can also be educational.

"PERSUASIVE COMMERCIAL"

Objective(s)

1. Students will create their own commercial informing others about measures to prevent contracting HIV/AIDS.

2. Students will present their final production to the class.

Materials Needed

- Video Camera
- TV/VCR/DVD
- Props for commercial
- Paper and pencils

Activity

1. Students will be placed in groups. They will first create a script concerning HIV/AIDS information to be presented to others their own age.

2. After the script is written videotaping will begin.

3. The final commercial video will be shared in class or other appropriate places.

Educational Theme

- We can educate ourselves and others about this disease through the creative use of mass media.

"AIDS MAPPING"

Objective(s)

1. Students will view the progression of how HIV can be spread throughout the population.
2. Students will describe how this chain of infection can be broken.

Materials Needed

- Chalkboard or whiteboard, chalk or markers, and eraser

Activity

1. Start a story on the chalkboard showing two people. Tell the students that they had unprotected sex and one is HIV positive.
2. Draw lines out from this couple and have them meet other individuals, and so on and so on.
3. After you create a map or picture of the potential spread of this virus ask the students what interventions could have been made?

Educational Theme

- Having unprotected sex can be far reaching in the population but can be avoided.

Resources

1. Bartholomew, L. K., Parcel, G. S., Kok, G. and Gottlieb, N. H. *Intervention Mapping*, Mountain View, CA: Mayfield Publishing, 2001.

"THE ORIGIN OF HIV/AIDS"

Objective(s)

1. Students will select a theory to review on the origin of HIV/AIDS.

2. Students will develop a one page written report on the subject.

Materials Needed

- Computer
- Internet
- Library resources

Activity

1. Students will be divided into groups to research the origin of HIV/AIDS. Some theories to review include (but are not limited too) a virus made for germ warfare, started in chimpanzees and moved to humans, HIV has been with us for many years and finally mutated into some deadly, etc.

2. Students will develop a one page (or more) typed report on their findings.

Educational Theme

- The origin of HIV/AIDS is still debated and we may never know the answer.

Resources

1. Internet and local library resources

2. Stine, G. *AIDS Update 2009*. Boston: McGraw Hill, 2009.

"HIV/AIDS ACRONYMS"

Objective(s)

1. Students will design and list acronyms from words involving the study of HIV/AIDS.

Materials Needed

- Paper and pencil

Activity

1. Have the students get into teams and develop their own list of acronyms using words involving the study of HIV/AIDS. Give the teams ten minutes to generate their word lists.

2. Examples:

   A-abstinence prevents disease
   I-information is the key to safety
   D-don't use natural or animal skin condoms during sex
   S-safer sex includes using a condom

   H-have fun but be safe in your behaviors
   I-if you don't have protection you should not have sex
   V-very important to learn about HIV/AIDS

Educational Theme

- This is a creative and fun way to use the information you have learned about HIV/AIDS.

Resources

1. Weeks, B. and Alcamo, I. *AIDS The Biological Basis*, (5th Ed.), Sudbury, MA: Jones and Bartlett, 2010.

"INHIBIT THE REPLICATION OF HIV"

Objective(s)

1. Students will demonstrate how anti-viral HIV/AIDS treatment medications work in the human body.

Materials Needed

➢ Chalkboard or whiteboard, chalk or markers, and eraser

Activity

1. Select two students from the class to help in the demonstration. Pull them aside and explain one student will write his or her name over and over on the board. The other student will from time to time take the strike out one of the names.

2. Explain to the class that this is how the replication of HIV is inhibited using reverse transcriptase inhibitors to interfere with the process. The instructor can then go into more detail on how these drugs work.

Educational Theme

➢ To help students understand how reverse transcriptase inhibitors work to fight the replication of the HIV.

Resources

1. Internet site www.aids.org

2. Internet site www.aidsmeds.com

"ANONYMOUS"

Objective(s)

1. Students will compose anonymous questions about HIV/AIDS.

2. This exercise will help break down fallacies, fears and misinformation about HIV/AIDS.

Materials Needed

- Hat or container

- Paper and pen or pencil

Activity

1. Have each student compose a question (with no names to identify the student) about HIV/AIDS on a small sheet of paper. Place all the questions in a hat or container.

2. Pass the questions around the room and have each student take a question. Read questions out loud (one at a time) and have the class answer the question (with the instructor's help if needed).

Educational Theme

- Using peers will begin to breakdown and barriers and fallacies about HIV/AIDS along with making the students more comfortable about the subject.

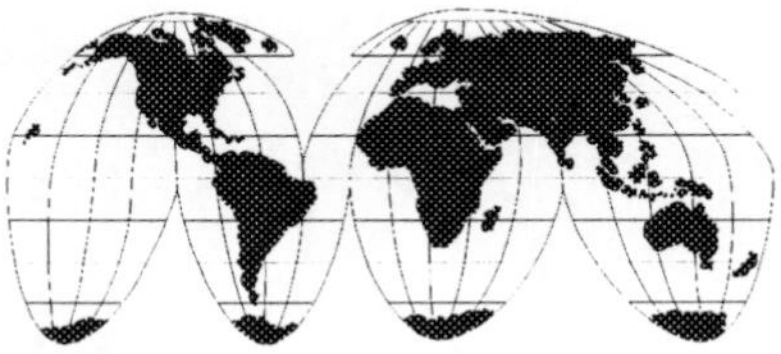

"SELECT A COUNTRY"

Objective(s)

1. Students will select a country to study the effects of HIV/AIDS on the population.

2. Students will develop a one page written report on the subject.

Materials Needed

- Computer
- Internet
- Library resources

Activity

1. Students will select a country of interest to research how HIV/AIDS effect the population living there. Areas covered could include: HIV/AIDS rates in the population, prevention efforts being made, availability of HIV/AIDS medications, etc.

2. Students will develop a one page (or more) typed report on their findings.

Educational Theme

- HIV/AIDS expresses itself differently throughout the globe.

Resources

1. Internet and local library resources

"FIGHTING PREJUDICE AND STIGMAS"

Objective(s)

1. Students will identify prejudices and stigmas associated with persons living with HIV disease.

2. Students will plan ways to combat prejudice and stigmas involving persons living with HIV disease.

Materials Needed

➢ Chalkboard or whiteboard, chalk or markers, and eraser

Activity

1. Pose a question to the students about how they think people would be treated living with HIV disease in their communities.

2. On the board create a listing of what students believe HIV positive people would have to face regarding employment, housing, education, and insurance in their community.

3. Discuss ways to decrease the stigma and prejudice towards individuals living with HIV disease.

Educational Theme

➢ To understand and predict how people living with HIV disease would be treated in their community and ways students could help fight potential discrimination.

Resources

1. Internet web site Averting HIV and AIDS www.vert.org

2. Internet web site Transforming The UK's Response to HIV www.areyouhivprejudiced.org

ABOUT THE AUTHOR

Dr. Minelli is currently a professor and former chair at Central Michigan University (CMU) and adjunct professor at Capella University. He was previously the director of Substance Abuse Services, Inc., in Ludington, Michigan, and has extensive experience in both outpatient counseling and prevention services. For ten years Dr. Minelli coordinated the CMU alcohol and other drug prevention program which was ranked in the top university prevention programs in the United States.

Dr. Minelli has written eight books/instructor manuals and over 30 journal/magazine/newspaper articles. He is considered to be one of the leading international experts on performance-enhancing drugs in sports and is an invited guest to many radio talk shows, conferences and newspaper interviews. Dr. Minelli has been awarded millions of dollars in funded grants/contracts on a wide variety of health related topics.

His most recent book "Community Health Education: Settings, Roles, and Skills" fifth edition, 2009, co-authored by Donald J. Breckon has been a standard training book for health educators for years. He and his wife Debra have four children, one grandchild and reside in Mt. Pleasant, Michigan.

SPECIAL THANKS TO THE REVIEWERS AND CONTRIBUTORS

Reviewers

Ernest Minelli, Ed.D.
Professor and Vice Provost Emeritus
Central Michigan University

Ross Rapaport, Ph.D.
Professor of Counseling
Central Michigan University

Contributors

Matt Calfin, B.S.
CMU Alumni

M. H. "Mark" Jones, M.A.
PWA

Jason Laker, B.S.
CMU Alumni

Jane Ruehle, M.Ed.
Prevention Planner

David Urlaub, M.A.
CMU Alumni

Holly Whitehead
CMU Alumni & Consultant

Beyond Beer Goggles Suggested Internet Resource Sites

To enhance your learning the following is a listing of internet web sites you may find helpful.

Government Organizations and Nonprofit Agencies

National Institutes of Health
http://www.nih/gov/

U.S. Department of Health and Human Services
http://www.os.dhhs.gov/

Indian Health Service
http://www.ihs.gov/

Office of Minority Health
http://www.omhrc.gov

Substance Abuse and Mental Health Services Administration
http://www.samhsa.gov/

Centers for Disease Control and Prevention
http://www.cdc.gov/

World Health Organization
http://www.who.org

Pan American Health Organization
http://www.paho.org

American Cancer Society
http://www.cancer.org

National Center for Health Statistics
http://www.cdc.gov/nchswww/nchshome.htm

Food and Drug Administration
http://www.fda.gov

Healthy People 2010
http://www.health.gov/healthypeople

Society for Public Health Education
http://www.sophe.org

State Health Departments on the World Wide Web
http://www.astho.org/state.html

United States Public Health Service
http://www.phs.os.dhhs.gov

Alcohol and Other Drug Information

Prevention Online (PREVLINE)
www.health.org

Join Together
www.jointogether.org

The BACCUS and GAMMA Peer Education Network
www.bacchusgamma.org

The National Association of State Alcohol and Drug Abuse Directors
www.nasadad.org

The National Center on Addiction and Substance Abuse at Columbia University
www.casacolumbia.org

Alcoholics Anonymous
www.alcoholics-anonymous.org

Adult Children of Alcoholics
www.adultchildren.org

Al-Anon/Alateen
www.al-anon.org

Narcotics Anonymous
www.na.org

DrugHelp
www.drughelp.org

The Community Anti-Drug Coalitions of America
www.cadca.org

Tobacco/Smoking Information

Tobacco Information and Prevention Source (TIPS)
www.cdc.gov/tobacco/index.htm

Action on Smoking and Health
www.ash.org
Children Opposed to Smoking Tobacco
www.costkids.org

GLOBALink is the International Tobacco Control Network
www.golbalink.org/gobdemo

Quit Net
www.quitnet.org

The Foundation for a Smokefree American
www.tobaccofree.org

HIV/AIDS Information

AIDS.ORG
www.aids.org

AIDS Meds
www.aidsmeds.com

POZ
www.poz.com

AIDS Healthcare Foundation
www.aidshealth.org

Averting HIV and AIDS
www.avert.org

AIDS.GOV
www.aids.gov

Medical Information

Web MD
www.webmd.com/

Weil Lifestyle, LLC
www.drweil.com/

Healthwise Knowledgebase
www.peacehealth.org/kase/

References

Bensley, R., and Brookins-Fisher, J. *Community Health Education Methods: A Practical Guide*, (2nd Ed.), Sudbury, MA: Jones and Bartlett, 2003.

Minelli, M., and Breckon, D. *Community Health Education: Settings Roles and Skills*, (5th Ed.), Sudbury, MA: Jones and Bartlett, 2009.

Minelli, M., Ledlow, G., and King, T. "Hot Sites From A To Z," *EAP Digest*. 21 (2001):28-30.

Minelli , M. *The Art of Living: Pathways to Personal Growth*, (2nd Ed.), Champaign, IL: Stipes Publishing Company, 2007.

Miller, D., and Price, J. *Dimensions of Community Health*, (5th ed.), Boston: WCB McGraw-Hill, 1998.